FOR EACH OF THE FOLLOWING DRAWINGS, CREATE AN AN AUXILIARY VIEW OF THE INDICATED INCLINED SURFACES.

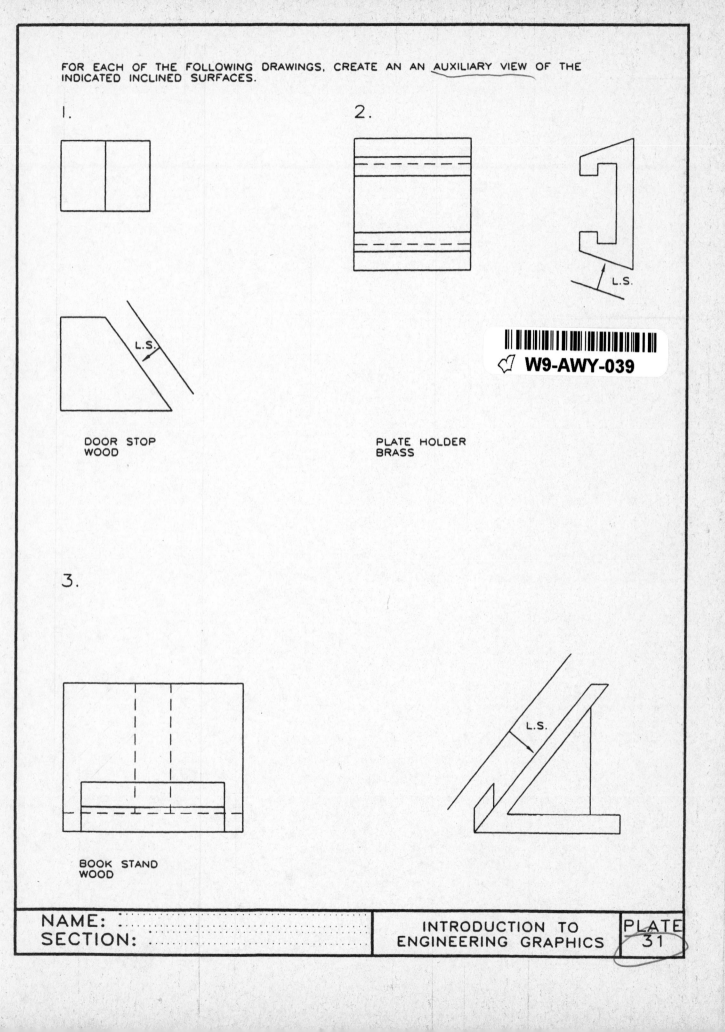

1.

2.

L.S.

L.S.

DOOR STOP
WOOD

PLATE HOLDER
BRASS

W9-AWY-039

3.

L.S.

BOOK STAND
WOOD

NAME: ....

SECTION: ....

INTRODUCTION TO
ENGINEERING GRAPHICS

PLATE
31

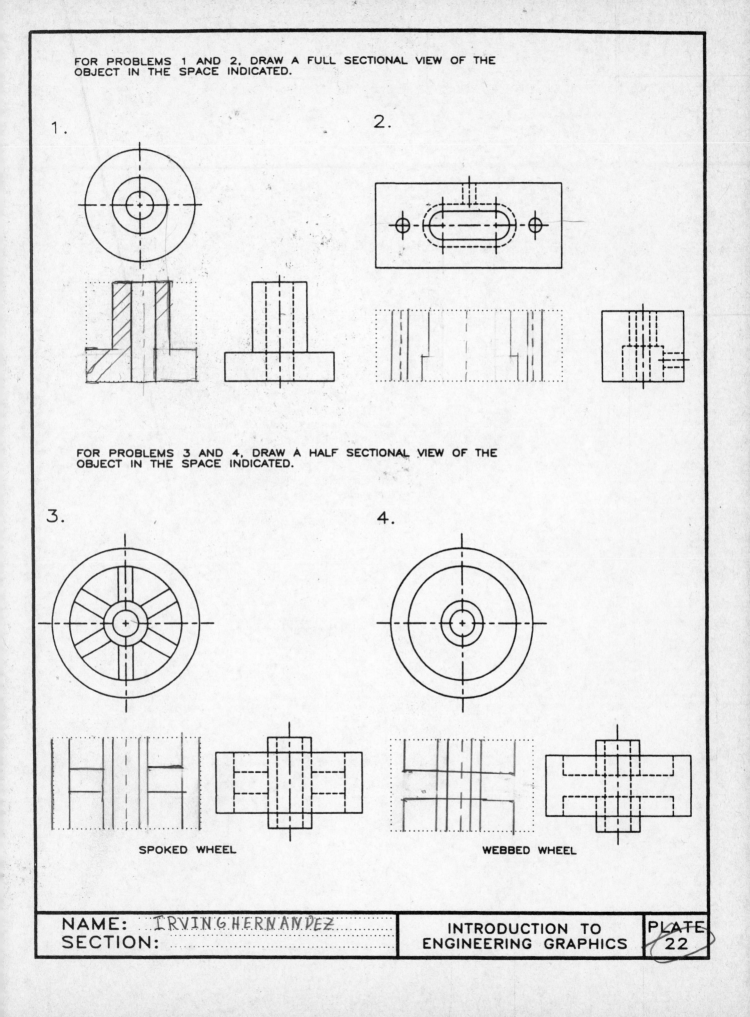

FOR PROBLEMS 1 AND 2, DRAW A FULL SECTIONAL VIEW OF THE OBJECT IN THE SPACE INDICATED.

1.

2.

FOR PROBLEMS 3 AND 4, DRAW A HALF SECTIONAL VIEW OF THE OBJECT IN THE SPACE INDICATED.

3.

4.

SPOKED WHEEL

WEBBED WHEEL

NAME: IRVING HERNANDEZ

SECTION:

INTRODUCTION TO ENGINEERING GRAPHICS

PLATE 22

Back of
Ch. 7
Do an ortho
top-front-sideview

Engineering Drawing

Problem Series 3

Taken From:

Engineering Drawing: Problem Series 3, Third Edition
by Paige Davis and Karen Reneé Juneau

PEARSON
Custom
Publishing

PEARSON
Prentice
Hall

Cover image: Ignition 9, by Mark Kelly

Taken from:

Engineering Drawing: Problem Series 3, Third Edition
by Paige Davis and Karen Reneé Juneau
Copyright © 2003, 2000, 1998 by Pearson Education, Inc.
Published by Prentice Hall
Upper Saddle River, New Jersey 07458

All rights reserved. No part of this book may be reproduced, in any form or by any means, without permission in writing from the publisher.

This special edition published in cooperation with Pearson Custom Publishing.

All trademarks, service marks, registered trademarks, and registered service marks are the property of their respective owners and are used herein for identification purposes only.

Printed in the United States of America

10

ISBN 0-536-44176-6

2007200230

SB

Please visit our web site at *www.pearsoncustom.com*

PEARSON CUSTOM PUBLISHING
501 Boylston Street, Suite 900, Boston, MA 02116
A Pearson Education Company

Preface

In this third edition of *Engineering Drawing Problem Series 3*, several changes have been made. Due to the widespread industry use of CAD and the declining use of traditional board drafting techniques, a larger portion of the text is now dedicated to sketching problems rather than instrument drafting problems. This allows the instructor to introduce many drafting concepts before assigning related CAD problems, even when a traditional drafting facility is not available. This workbook also includes additional problem sets and many plates have been revised since the first edition.

Many engineering graphic courses serve students from many diverse fields such as landscape architecture, interior design, and graphic design. In some cases, only one semester of graphics is required as part of a degree program. These students are interested in learning the basics of the orthographic drawing and computer assisted design. In one semester, students expect to gain enough expertise in CAD and in engineering graphics to be able to apply these skills effectively in their respective fields. This workbook is intended to be used in such a course: a one-semester introductory course that includes 2D-CAD and basic graphical concepts.

Although the topics in this workbook form the core of many engineering graphics courses, we have chosen to use as many commonly found objects as possible to make these concepts more assessable to all students. The inclusion of a CD with exercises and predefined problems allows the beginning student to make the most effective use of computer time by reducing the time it takes to set up a problem.

This work is under continuous review and revision. This workbook has been used successfully in university engineering graphics courses and in introductory community college courses in drafting fundamentals. It is hoped that other instructors will find this work useful in similar courses. Any questions or comments that would help us improve this work would be greatly appreciated.

PAIGE R. DAVIS
Louisiana State University
Baton Rouge, LA

KAREN R. JUNEAU
University of Southern Mississippi
Hattiesburg, MS

TABLE OF CONTENTS

DRAWING PLATES

COMPUTER PLATES

DRAW OR SKETCH EACH LINE STYLE IN THE SPACE BELOW THE EXAMPLE.

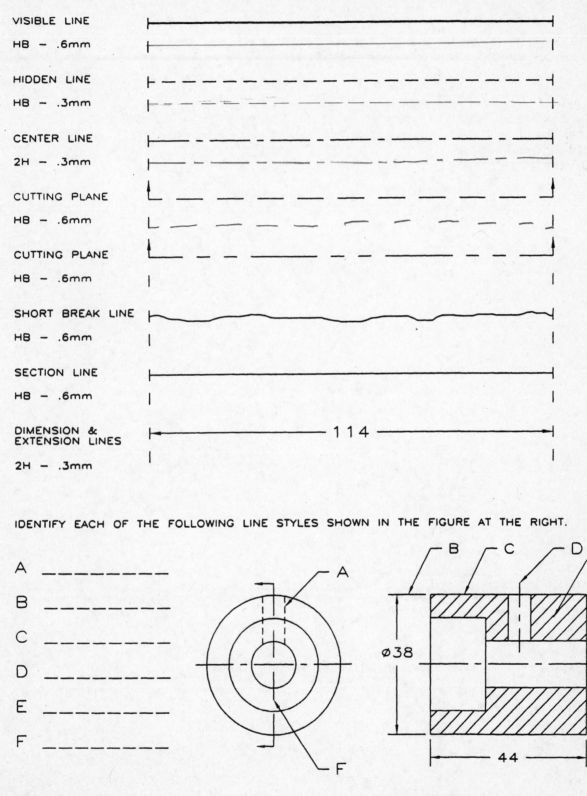

VISIBLE LINE
HB – .6mm

HIDDEN LINE
HB – .3mm

CENTER LINE
2H – .3mm

CUTTING PLANE
HB – .6mm

CUTTING PLANE
HB – .6mm

SHORT BREAK LINE
HB – .6mm

SECTION LINE
HB – .6mm

DIMENSION &
EXTENSION LINES
2H – .3mm

114

IDENTIFY EACH OF THE FOLLOWING LINE STYLES SHOWN IN THE FIGURE AT THE RIGHT.

A _____

B _____

C _____

D _____

E _____

F _____

A

F

B   C   D   E

Ø38

44

NAME: ....
SECTION: ....

INTRODUCTION TO
ENGINEERING GRAPHICS

PLATE
3

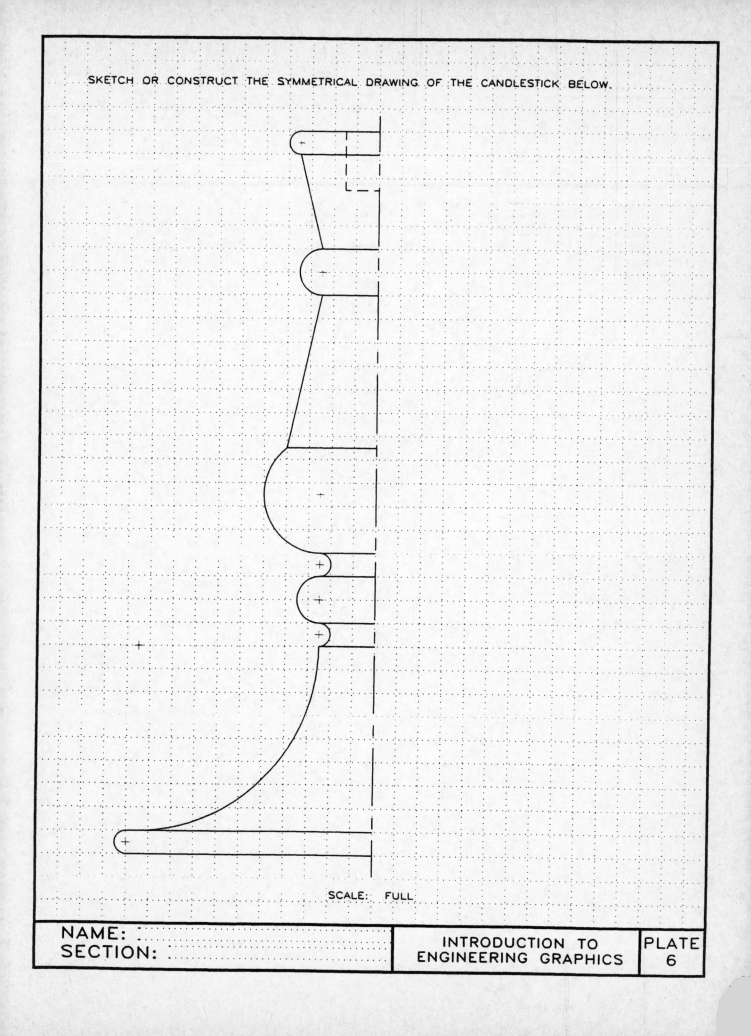

SKETCH OR CONSTRUCT THE SYMMETRICAL DRAWING OF THE CANDLESTICK BELOW.

SCALE: FULL

NAME:
SECTION:

INTRODUCTION TO
ENGINEERING GRAPHICS

PLATE
6

USE THE METRIC SCALE AND MEASURE THE DISTANCES A, B, C, AND D IN THE
TWO-VIEW DRAWING SHOWN BELOW.   BE SURE TO LETTER YOUR ANSWER.

	A(cm)	B(mm)	C(cm)	D(mm)
1. 1:10	....	....	....	....
2. 1:1	....	....	....	....
3. 1:2	....	....	....	....

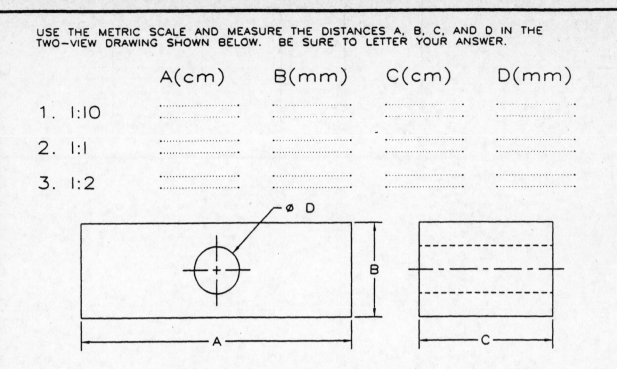

DRAW THE FOLLOWING LINES LISTED BELOW USING THE SPECIFIED SCALES.   A
STARTING POINT IS GIVEN FOR EACH PROBLEM.

4. 45mm   SCALE 1:1   ⊢

5. 3.1cm   SCALE 1:1   ⊢

6. 98mm   SCALE 1:2   ⊢

7. 6.6cm   SCALE 1:2   ⊢

DIMENSION THE BRACKET BELOW.   USE YOUR METRIC SCALE.   SCALE 1:1

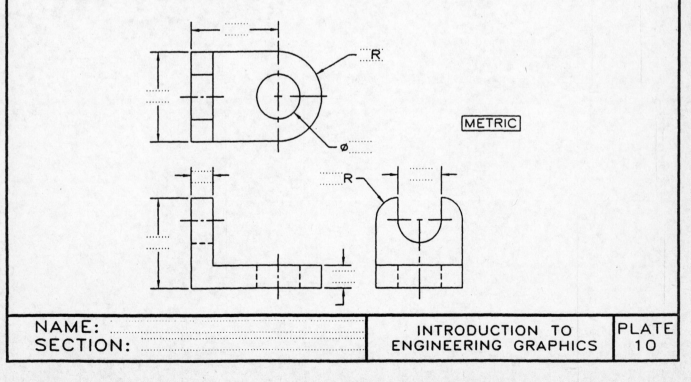

METRIC

USE THE METRIC SCALE AND MEASURE THE DISTANCES A, B, C, AND D IN THE
TWO-VIEW DRAWING SHOWN BELOW. BE SURE TO LETTER YOUR ANSWER.

	A(mm)	B(mm)	C(cm)	R(cm)
1. 1:10	....	....	....	....
2. 1:1	....	....	....	....
3. 1:2	....	....	....	....

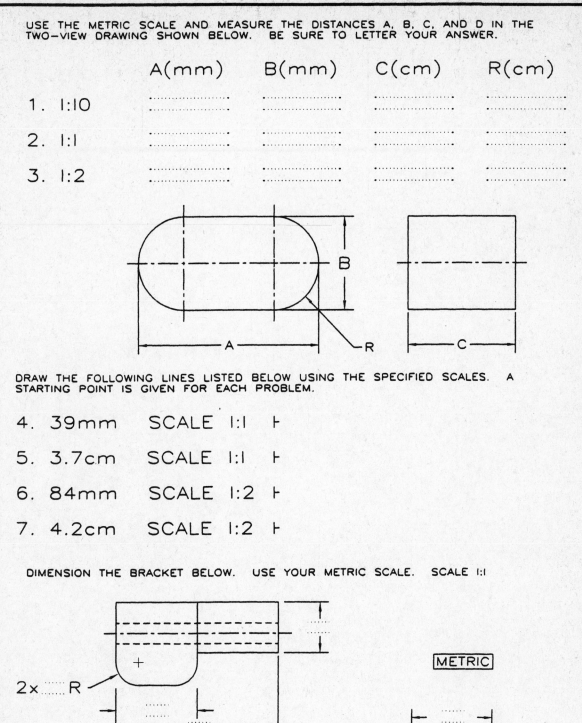

DRAW THE FOLLOWING LINES LISTED BELOW USING THE SPECIFIED SCALES. A
STARTING POINT IS GIVEN FOR EACH PROBLEM.

4. 39mm   SCALE 1:1   ⊢

5. 3.7cm   SCALE 1:1   ⊢

6. 84mm   SCALE 1:2   ⊢

7. 4.2cm   SCALE 1:2   ⊢

DIMENSION THE BRACKET BELOW. USE YOUR METRIC SCALE.   SCALE 1:1

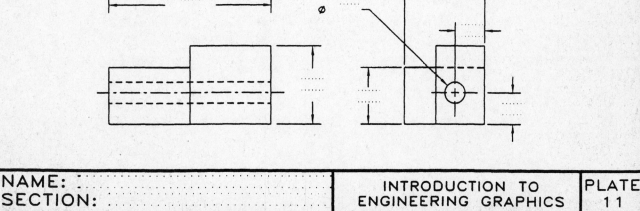

2x ...... R

METRIC

1.   - MARK THE LOCATION OF AN UNSEEN PLANET THAT IS HALFWAY BETWEEN THE
CENTER OF THE STAR AND THE CENTER OF LYRA AND MARK WITH A "Q".

      - THE PLANET YOU JUST LOCATED HAS THREE MOONS THAT MOVE IN A
CIRCULAR ORBIT AROUND IT. BASED ON THIS INFORMATION, IDENTIFY THE
PLANET THAT IS NOT A MOON AND LABEL IT "P".

      - IF THE JOURNEY FROM THE PLANET LYRA TO THE UNSEEN PLANET Q TAKES
THREE EQUAL TRAVEL DAYS, MARK THE DISTANCE TRAVELED BY THE END
OF THE SECOND DAY WITH A SHORT LINE LABELED "T".

2.   - THE FOLLOWING DRAWING IS A SITE LAYOUT FOR A HOUSE.
COMPLETE THE DRIVEWAY WITH A CURVED CORNER.   THE INSIDE
RADIUS OF THE CURVE IS 20 FEET.   MARK ALL TANGENT POINTS.

      - BECAUSE OF A PREVAILING NORTH WIND, THE OWNERS WOULD LIKE A ROW
OF THREE TREES PLANTED IN A DIAGONAL LINE ALONG THE BISECTOR OF THE
ANGLE FORMED BY THE HEDGE.

      - ALONG THE BISECTOR JUST LOCATED, MARK WITH AN "X" THE
LOCATION OF EACH OF THE THREE TREES IF THEY ARE TO BE EVENLY
SPACED AND IF THE LAST TREE IS TO BE LOCATED 55 FEET FROM THE
INTERSECTION OF THE HEDGES.

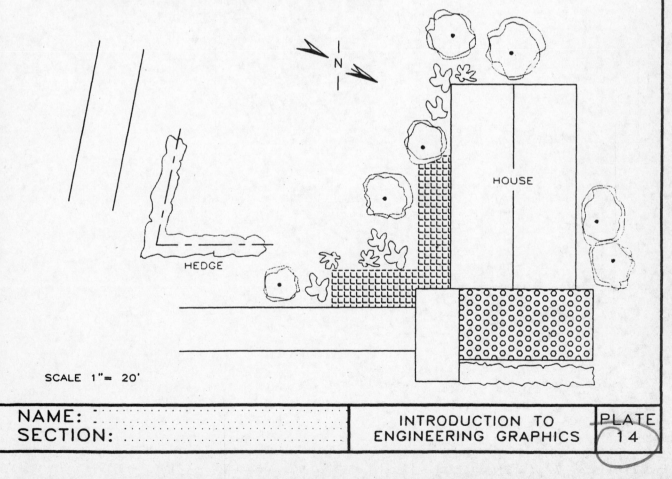

SCALE 1"= 20'

NAME: ....
SECTION: ....

INTRODUCTION TO
ENGINEERING GRAPHICS

PLATE
14

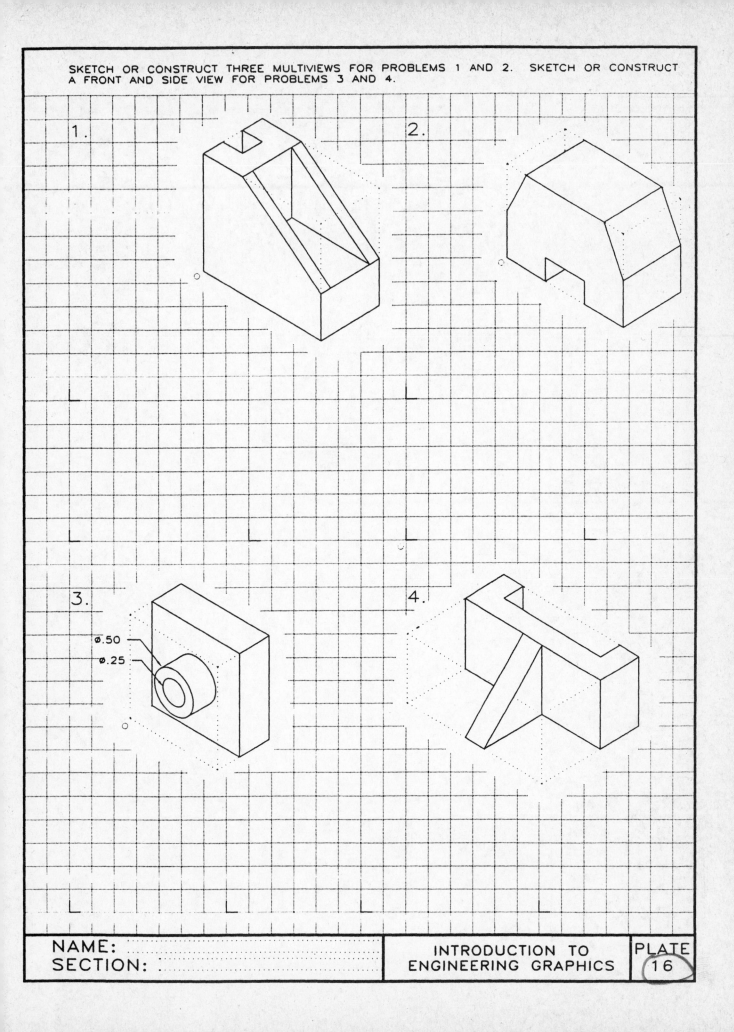

SKETCH OR CONSTRUCT THREE MULTIVIEWS FOR PROBLEMS 1 AND 2. SKETCH OR CONSTRUCT
A FRONT AND SIDE VIEW FOR PROBLEMS 3 AND 4.

1.

2.

3.

ø.50
ø.25

4.

NAME:
SECTION:

INTRODUCTION TO
ENGINEERING GRAPHICS

PLATE
16

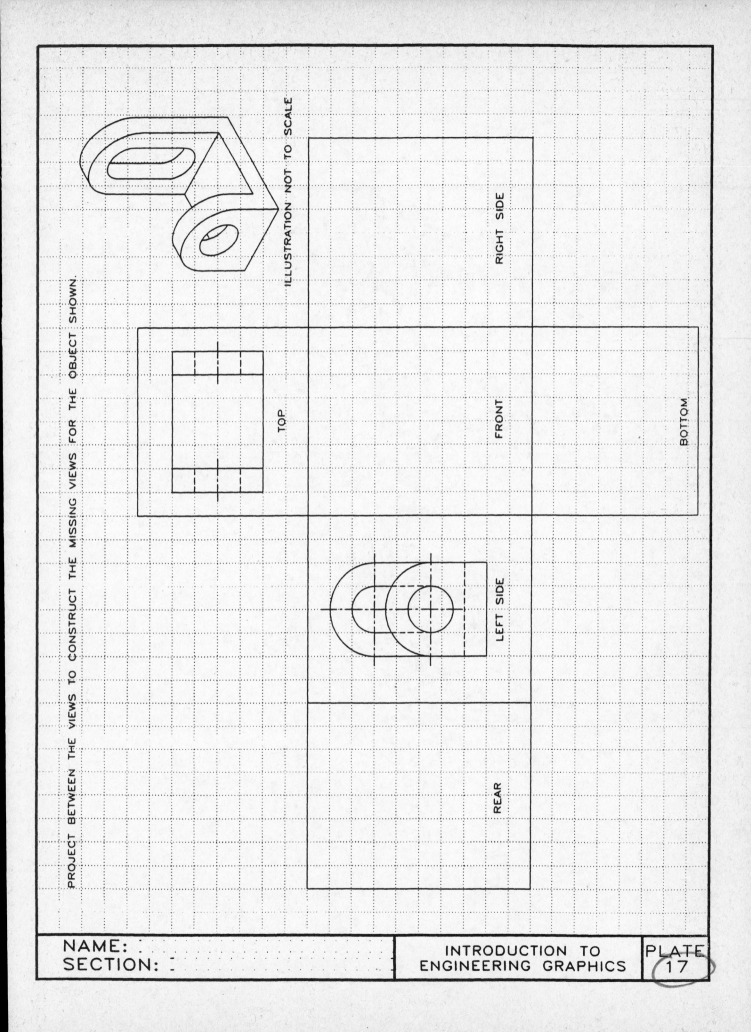

ILLUSTRATION NOT TO SCALE

PROJECT BETWEEN THE VIEWS TO CONSTRUCT THE MISSING VIEWS FOR THE OBJECT SHOWN.

RIGHT SIDE

TOP

FRONT

BOTTOM

LEFT SIDE

REAR

NAME:

SECTION:

INTRODUCTION TO
ENGINEERING GRAPHICS

PLATE
17

EACH OF THE FOLLOWING DRAWINGS IS INCOMPLETE. PLEASE ADD THE
NEEDED MISSING LINES TO COMPLETE THE VIEWS. YOU MAY NOT ADD ANY
LINES OUTSIDE OF THE EDGES OF THE PRESENT VIEWS. THE LINES MAY BE
HIDDEN LINES OR OBJECT LINES. PLEASE ADD CENTERLINES WHERE NEEDED.
IT IS OFTEN HELPFUL TO SKETCH THE OBJECT AND/OR TO NUMBER THE POINTS.

| NAME: | INTRODUCTION TO | PLATE |
| SECTION: | ENGINEERING GRAPHICS. | 19 |

EACH OF THE FOLLOWING DRAWINGS IS INCOMPLETE. PLEASE ADD THE
NEEDED MISSING LINES TO COMPLETE THE VIEWS. YOU MAY NOT ADD ANY
LINES OUTSIDE OF THE EDGES OF THE PRESENT VIEWS. THE LINES MAY BE
HIDDEN LINES OR OBJECT LINES. PLEASE ADD CENTERLINES WHERE NEEDED.
IT IS OFTEN HELPFUL TO SKETCH THE OBJECT AND/OR NUMBER THE POINTS.

CONSTRUCT THE FRONT AND SIDE VIEWS OF THE
LATCH PLATE SHOWN.

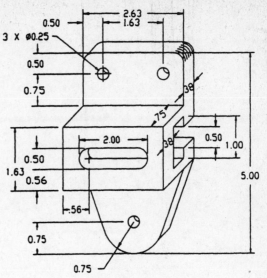

NAME: . . . .
SECTION: . . . .

INTRODUCTION TO
ENGINEERING GRAPHICS

PLATE
21

FOR PROBLEMS 1 AND 2, DRAW A FULL SECTIONAL VIEW OF THE OBJECT
IN THE INDICATED SPACE.   BE SURE TO INCLUDE THE CUTTING PLANE LINE.

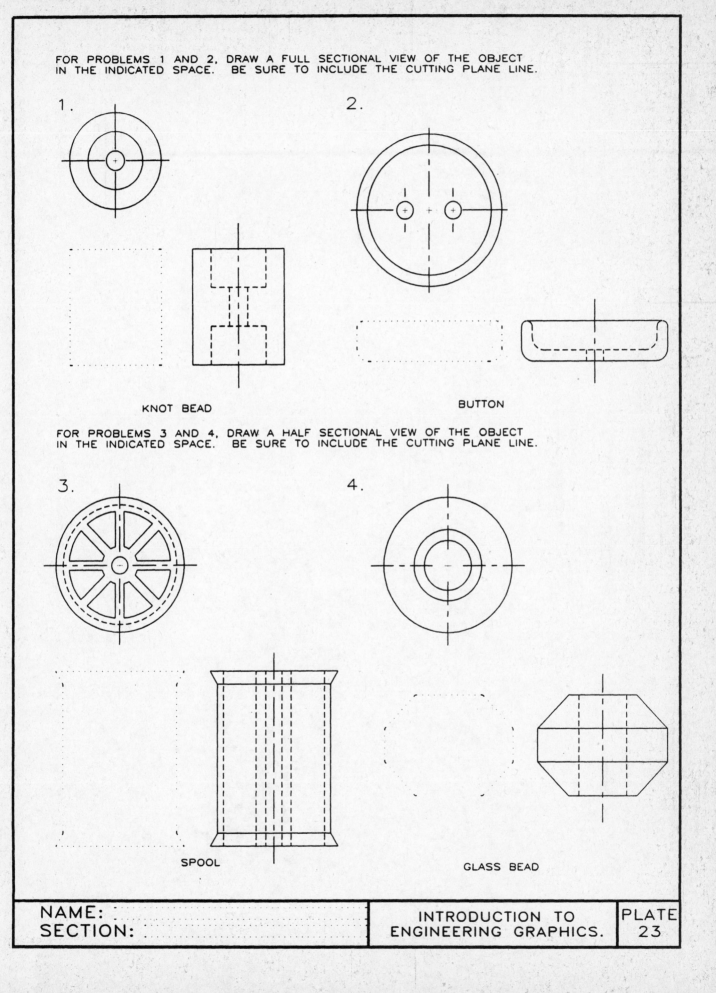

1.

KNOT BEAD

2.

BUTTON

FOR PROBLEMS 3 AND 4, DRAW A HALF SECTIONAL VIEW OF THE OBJECT
IN THE INDICATED SPACE.   BE SURE TO INCLUDE THE CUTTING PLANE LINE.

3.

SPOOL

4.

GLASS BEAD

NAME: ....
SECTION: ....

INTRODUCTION TO
ENGINEERING GRAPHICS.

PLATE
23

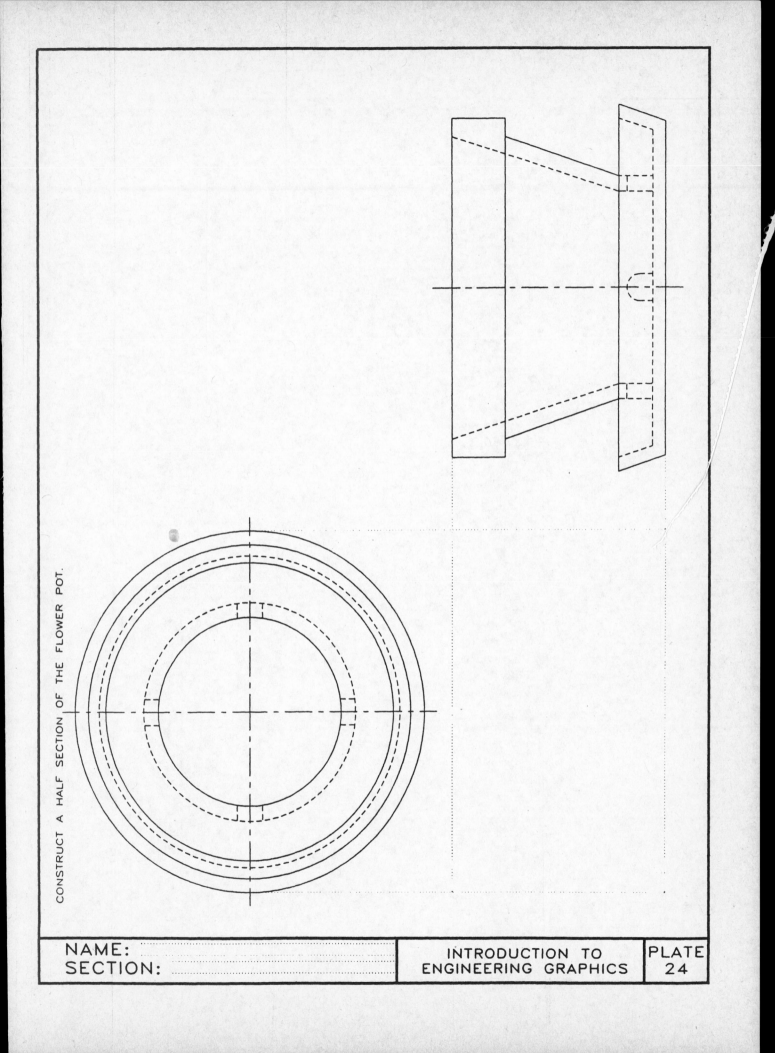

CONSTRUCT A HALF SECTION OF THE FLOWER POT.

NAME:

SECTION:

INTRODUCTION TO
ENGINEERING GRAPHICS

PLATE
24

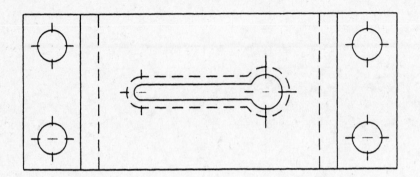

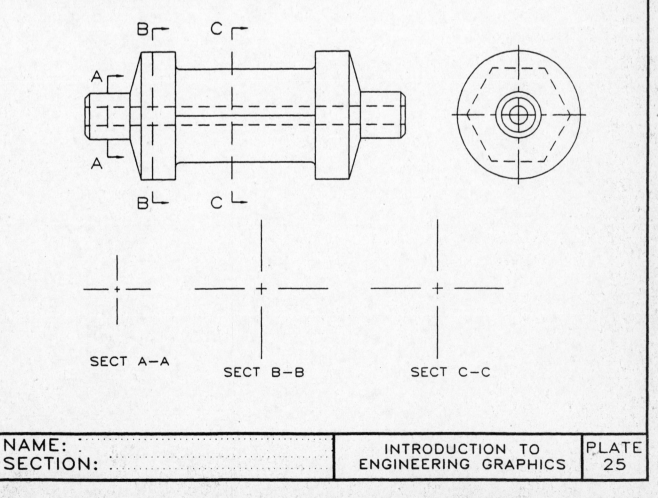

2. DRAW REMOVED SECTIONS FOR A-A, B-B, AND C-C.

SECT A-A

SECT B-B

SECT C-C

NAME:
SECTION:

INTRODUCTION TO
ENGINEERING GRAPHICS

PLATE
25

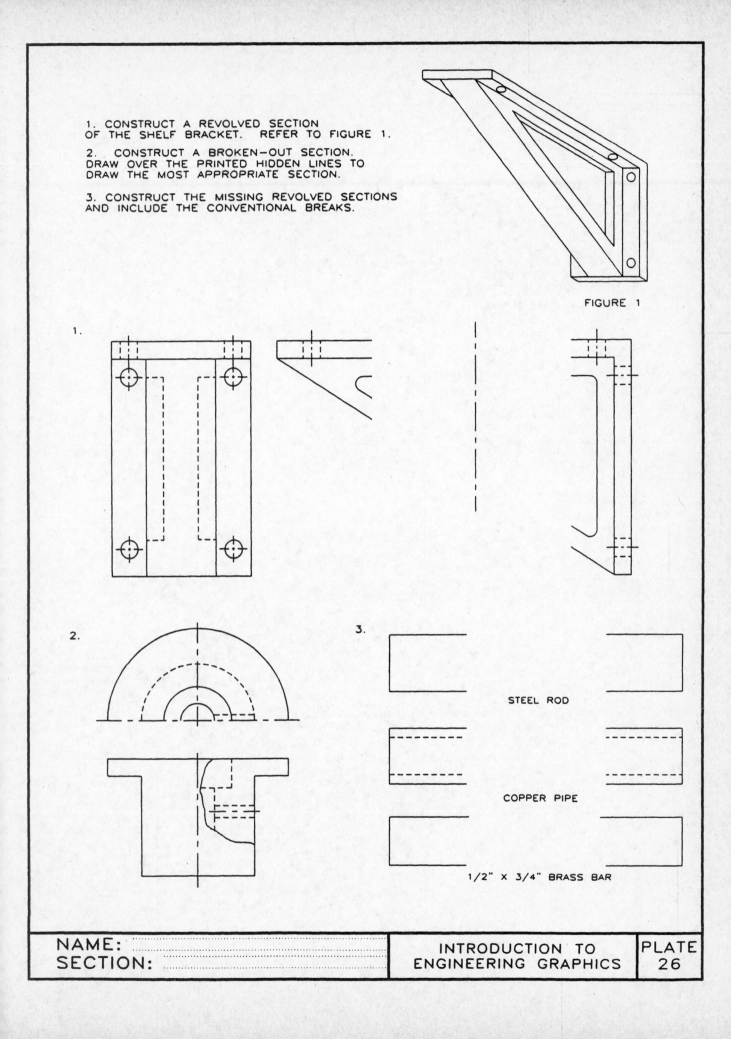

1. CONSTRUCT A REVOLVED SECTION OF THE SHELF BRACKET. REFER TO FIGURE 1.

2. CONSTRUCT A BROKEN-OUT SECTION. DRAW OVER THE PRINTED HIDDEN LINES TO DRAW THE MOST APPROPRIATE SECTION.

3. CONSTRUCT THE MISSING REVOLVED SECTIONS AND INCLUDE THE CONVENTIONAL BREAKS.

FIGURE 1

1.

2.

3.

STEEL ROD

COPPER PIPE

1/2" X 3/4" BRASS BAR

NAME:

SECTION:

INTRODUCTION TO ENGINEERING GRAPHICS

PLATE 26

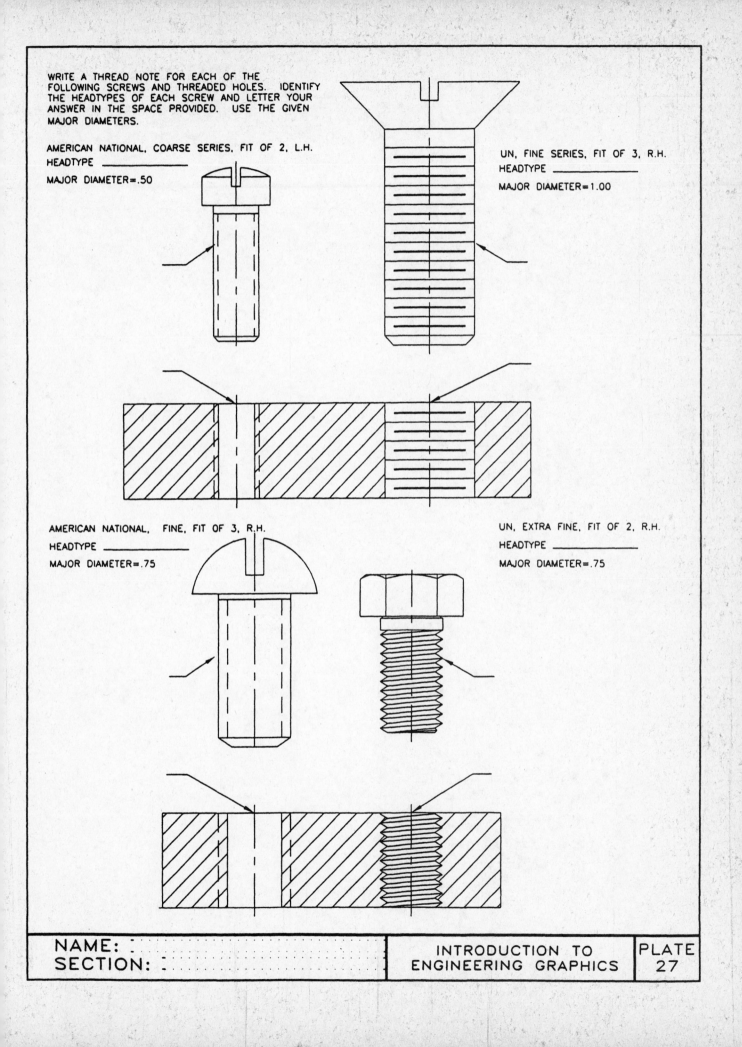

WRITE A THREAD NOTE FOR EACH OF THE
FOLLOWING SCREWS AND THREADED HOLES. IDENTIFY
THE HEADTYPES OF EACH SCREW AND LETTER YOUR
ANSWER IN THE SPACE PROVIDED. USE THE GIVEN
MAJOR DIAMETERS.

AMERICAN NATIONAL, COARSE SERIES, FIT OF 2, L.H.
HEADTYPE _____
MAJOR DIAMETER=.50

UN, FINE SERIES, FIT OF 3, R.H.
HEADTYPE _____
MAJOR DIAMETER=1.00

AMERICAN NATIONAL, FINE, FIT OF 3, R.H.
HEADTYPE _____
MAJOR DIAMETER=.75

UN, EXTRA FINE, FIT OF 2, R.H.
HEADTYPE _____
MAJOR DIAMETER=.75

NAME: ⁚ . . . .
SECTION: ⁚ . . . .

INTRODUCTION TO
ENGINEERING GRAPHICS

PLATE
27

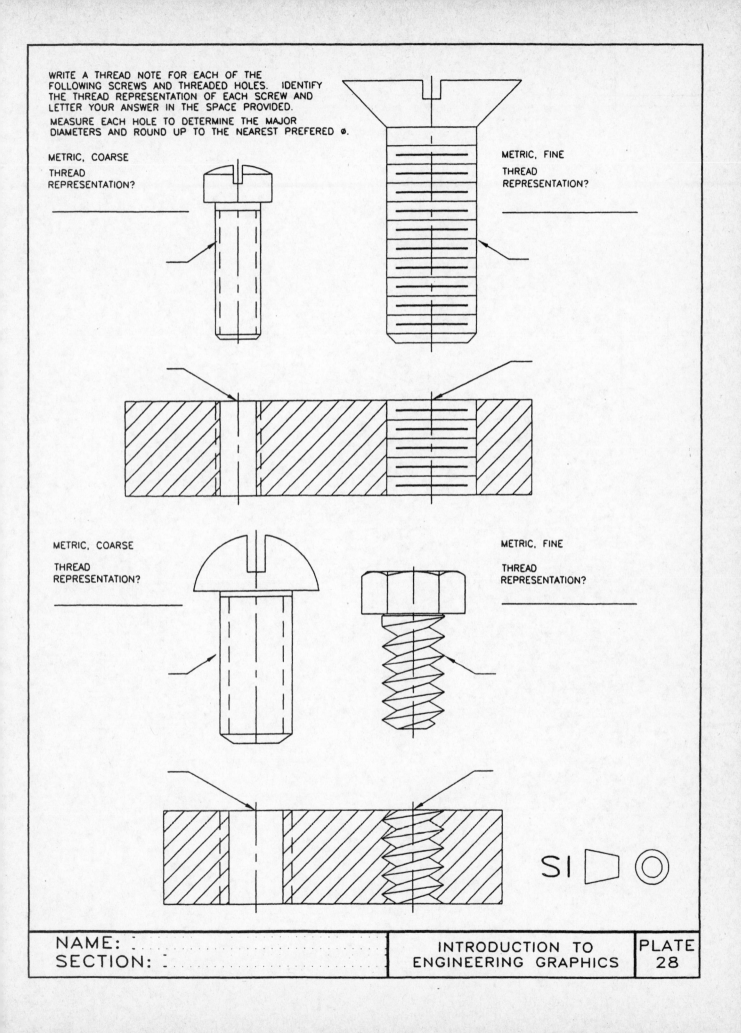

WRITE A THREAD NOTE FOR EACH OF THE
FOLLOWING SCREWS AND THREADED HOLES. IDENTIFY
THE THREAD REPRESENTATION OF EACH SCREW AND
LETTER YOUR ANSWER IN THE SPACE PROVIDED.
MEASURE EACH HOLE TO DETERMINE THE MAJOR
DIAMETERS AND ROUND UP TO THE NEAREST PREFERED ⌀.

METRIC, COARSE
THREAD
REPRESENTATION?
_____

METRIC, FINE
THREAD
REPRESENTATION?
_____

METRIC, COARSE
THREAD
REPRESENTATION?
_____

METRIC, FINE
THREAD
REPRESENTATION?
_____

SI

NAME:
SECTION:

INTRODUCTION TO
ENGINEERING GRAPHICS

PLATE
28

COMPLETE THE THREADS BELOW IN THE GIVEN REPRESENTATION.   WRITE A THREAD NOTE FOR
EACH THREAD.   DRAW THREADS FROM POINT O TO THE CHAMFER FOR EACH PROBLEM.

PROBLEM 1. SCHEMATIC REPRESENTATION.
UNC, FIT OF 2, L.H..

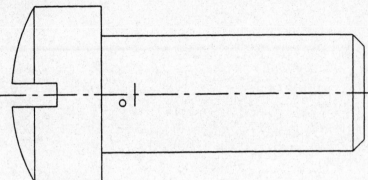

PROBLEM 2. SIMPLIFIED REPRESENTATION
METRIC, FINE

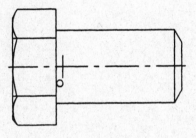

PROBLEM 3.   DRAW SIMPLIFIED SECTIONAL VIEWS OF THE FOLLOWING THREE HOLES.   BE
SURE TO EXTEND SECTION LINES TO COMPLETE THE VIEW.   ADD LEADERS FOR THE NOTES.

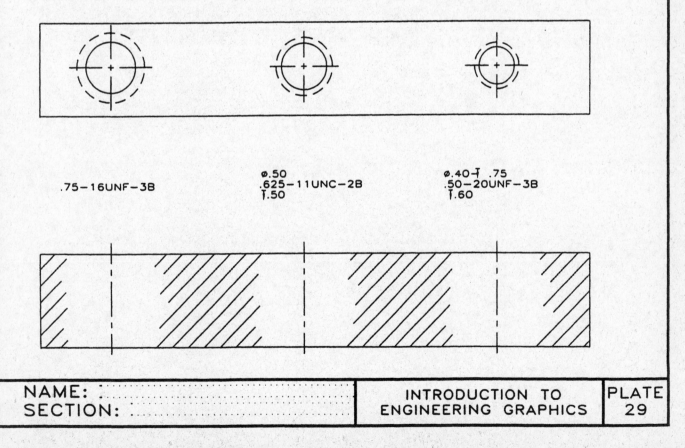

.75-16UNF-3B

Ø.50
.625-11UNC-2B
↧.50

Ø.40↧.75
.50-20UNF-3B
↧.60

PROBLEM I. COMPLETE THE PARTIALLY DRAWN VIEW OF THE HEX HEAD BOLT,
DRAW DETAILED THREADS TO POINT O FOR A 1-INCH DIAMETER, UNC, FIT OF 3.
YOU WILL NEED TO EXTEND THE GIVEN LINES AND INCLUDE A THREAD NOTE.
INCLUDE A 45° CHAMFER AT THE END OF THE BOLT.

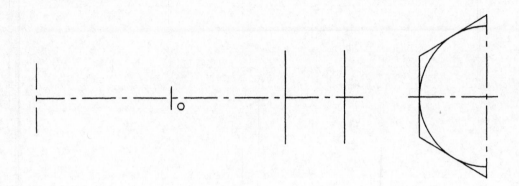

STUDY THE FOLLOWING THREAD REPRESENTATIONS AND ANSWER THE QUESTIONS.

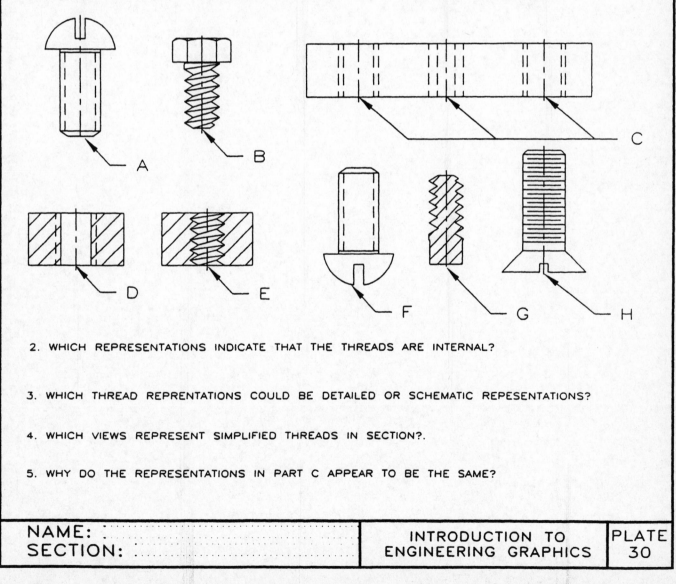

2. WHICH REPRESENTATIONS INDICATE THAT THE THREADS ARE INTERNAL?

3. WHICH THREAD REPRENTATIONS COULD BE DETAILED OR SCHEMATIC REPESENTATIONS?

4. WHICH VIEWS REPRESENT SIMPLIFIED THREADS IN SECTION?.

5. WHY DO THE REPRESENTATIONS IN PART C APPEAR TO BE THE SAME?

NAME: :...............................
SECTION: :...............................

INTRODUCTION TO
ENGINEERING GRAPHICS

PLATE
30

DRAW AN AUXILARY VIEW OF THE INDICATED INCLINED SURFACES ONLY FOR EACH OBJECT.

1.

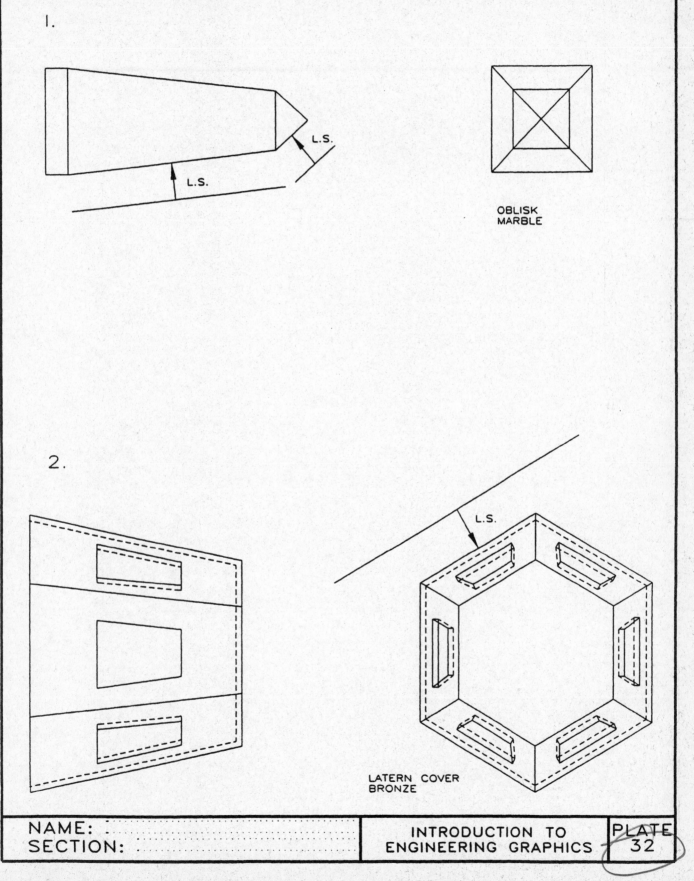

L.S.

L.S.

OBLISK
MARBLE

2.

L.S.

LATERN COVER
BRONZE

NAME: ....
SECTION: ....

INTRODUCTION TO
ENGINEERING GRAPHICS

PLATE
32

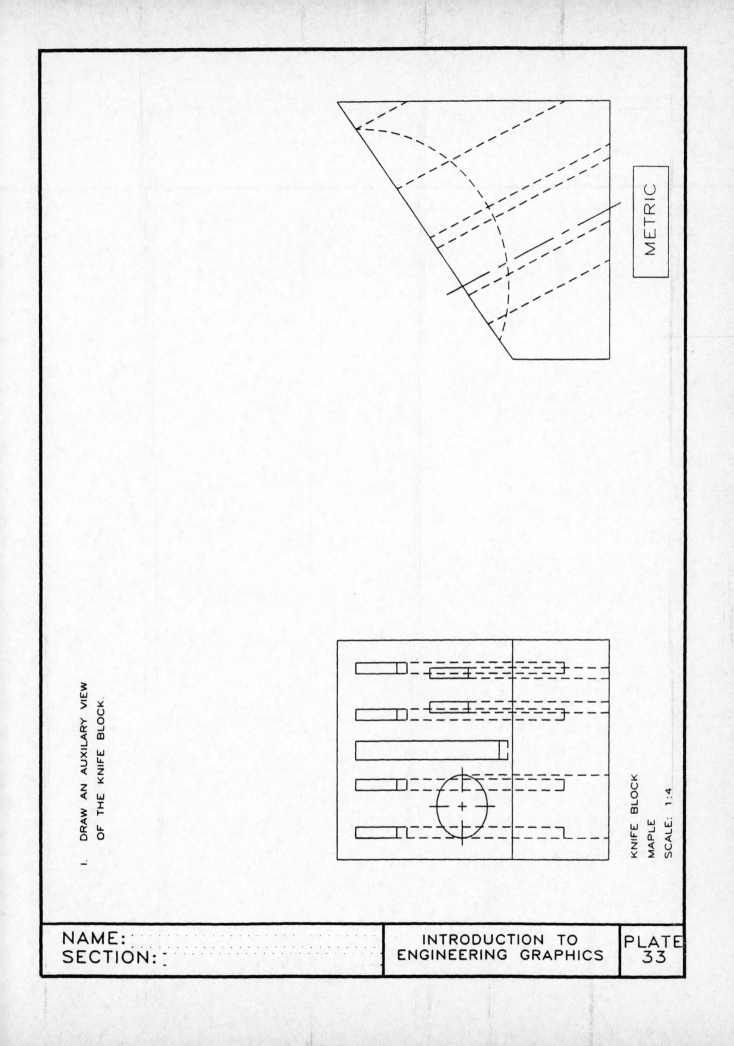

METRIC

1. DRAW AN AUXILARY VIEW
   OF THE KNIFE BLOCK.

KNIFE BLOCK
MAPLE
SCALE: 1:4

NAME:
SECTION:

INTRODUCTION TO
ENGINEERING GRAPHICS

PLATE
33

DIMENSION THE FOLLOWING OBJECTS IN THE GIVEN SCALES.

1.

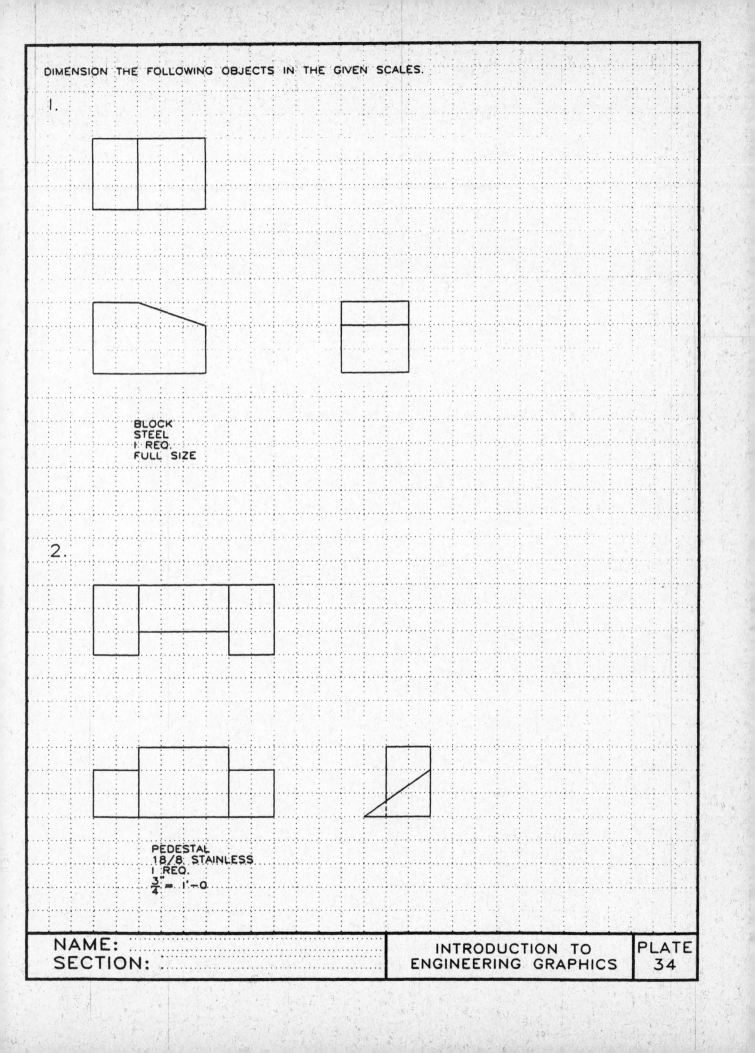

BLOCK
STEEL
1 REQ.
FULL SIZE

2.

PEDESTAL
18/8 STAINLESS
1 REQ.
$\frac{3"}{4} = 1'-0$

NAME: ....
SECTION: ....

INTRODUCTION TO
ENGINEERING GRAPHICS

PLATE
34

DIMENSION THE FOLLOWING OBJECTS IN THE GIVEN SCALES.

1.

MOUSE PAD
1:4

2.

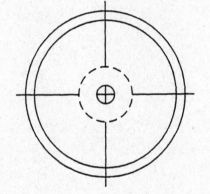

3.

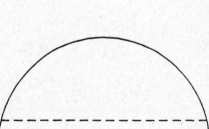

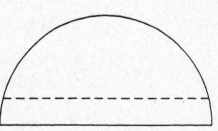

NAPKIN HOLDER
1:2

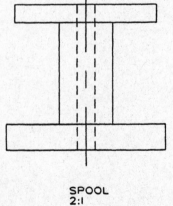

SPOOL
2:1

SI

NAME: ....

SECTION: ....

INTRODUCTION TO
ENGINEERING GRAPHICS

PLATE
35

PLEASE DIMENSION THE FOLLOWING OBJECTS IN THE GIVEN SCALES.

1.

2.

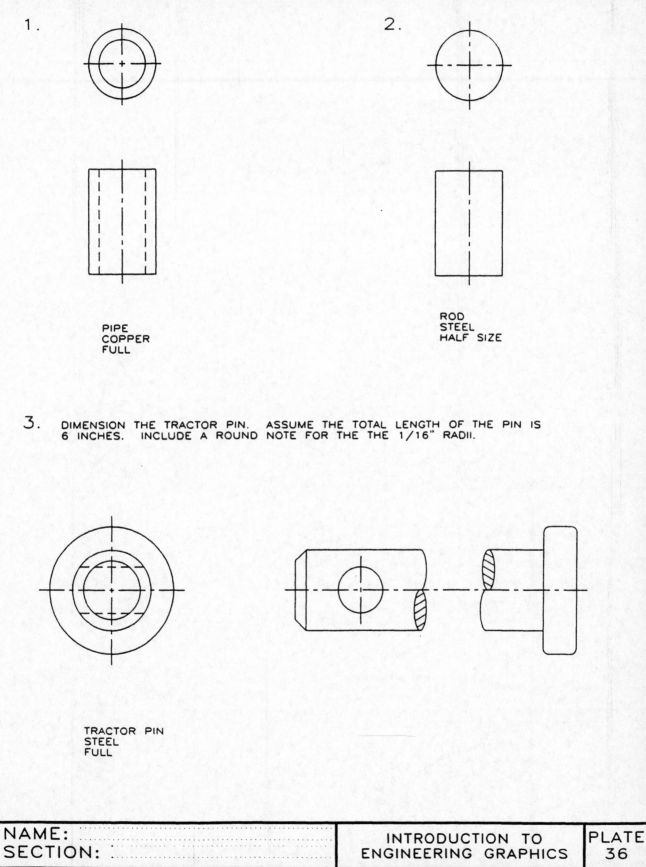

PIPE
COPPER
FULL

ROD
STEEL
HALF SIZE

3. DIMENSION THE TRACTOR PIN. ASSUME THE TOTAL LENGTH OF THE PIN IS
6 INCHES. INCLUDE A ROUND NOTE FOR THE THE 1/16" RADII.

TRACTOR PIN
STEEL
FULL

DIMENSION THE FOLLOWING MACHINED HOLES BY NOTE IN MILLIMETERS.

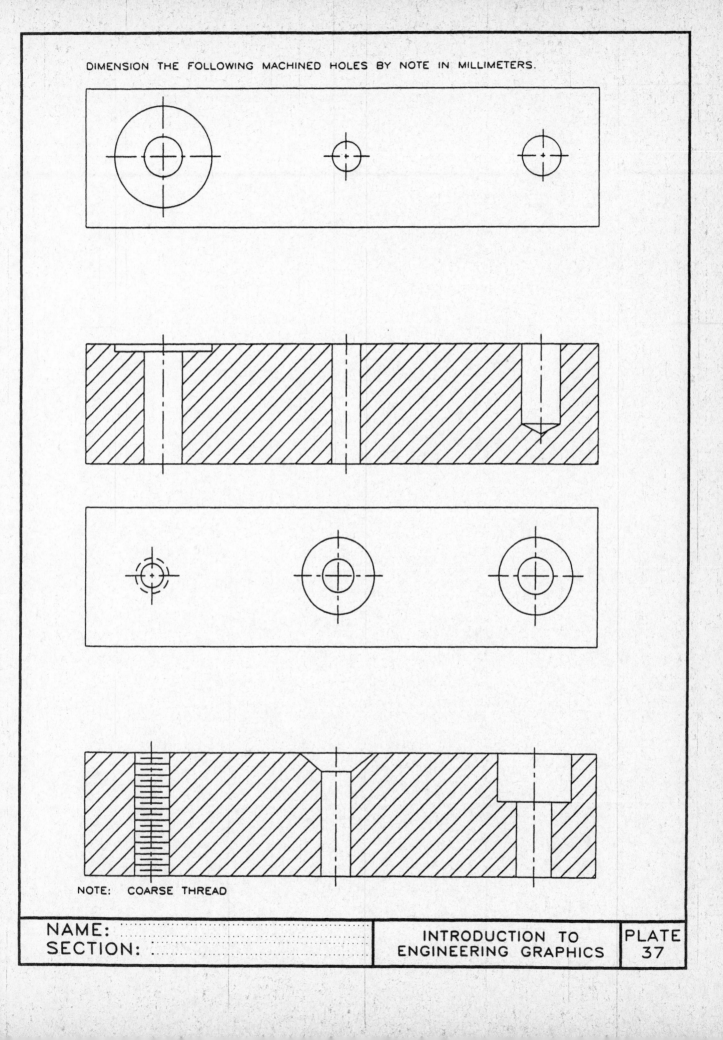

NOTE: COARSE THREAD

DIMENSION THE OBJECT BELOW. INCLUDE MACHINED HOLE NOTES,
A ROUND NOTE AND THE LOCATION DIMENSIONS. THE
SCALE OF THE DRAWING IS 1:1 MILLIMETERS.

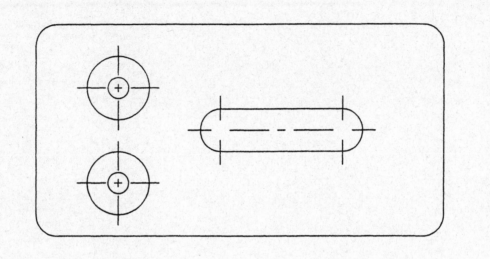

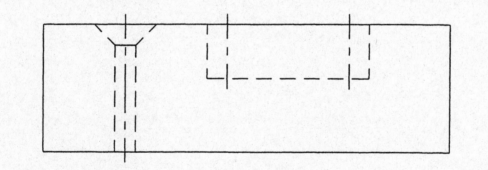

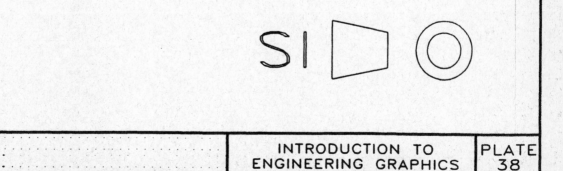

DIMENSION ONLY THE MACHINED FEATURES ON THE FOLLOWING OBJECTS.
ALL OBJECTS ARE DRAWN IN MILLIMETERS AT SCALE OF 1:1.

PROBLEM 1.
DIMENSION THE KNURL.
THE PITCH IS 0.8.

PROBLEM 2.
DIMENSION THE KNURL.
THE PITCH IS 64 DP.

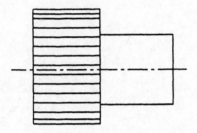

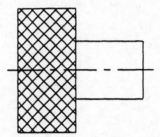

PROBLEM 3.
COMPLETELY DIMENSION THE SPINDLE, INCLUDING THE GROOVES AND THE CHAMFERS.

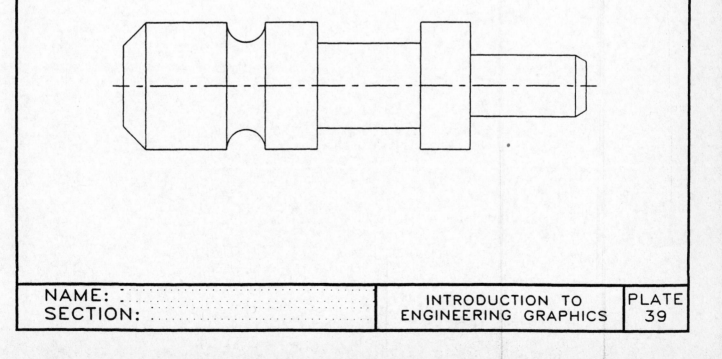

NAME: ....

SECTION: ....

INTRODUCTION TO
ENGINEERING GRAPHICS

PLATE
39

DIMENSION THE DRAWING OF THE LATCH PLATE.   COMPLETE THE RIGHT SIDE VIEW AS
AN OFFSET SECTION.   BE SURE TO INCLUDE A CUTTING PLANE LINE.

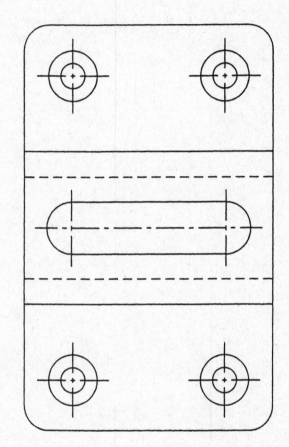

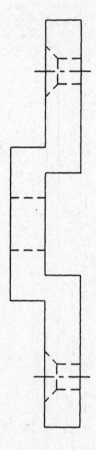

SI ▷ ◯

DIMENSION THE FOLLOWING OBJECTS.   MEASURE THE DRAWINGS TO DETERMINE THE BASIC
SIZE AND CALCULATE THE LIMITS FOR EACH FIT.

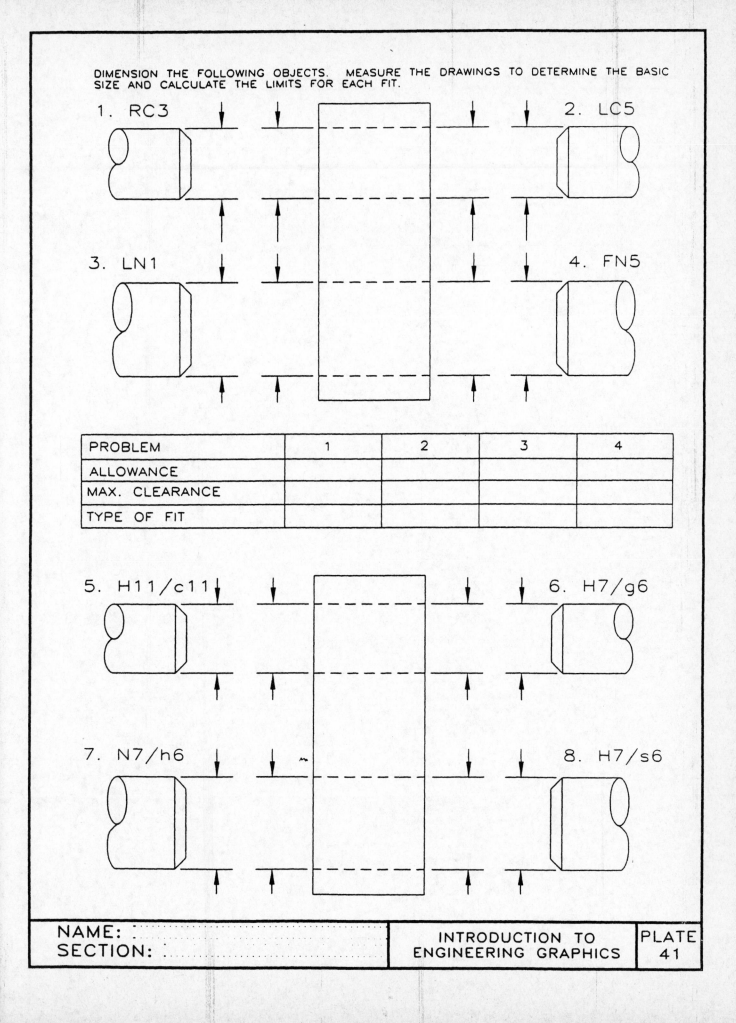

1. RC3

2. LC5

3. LN1

4. FN5

PROBLEM	1	2	3	4
ALLOWANCE				
MAX. CLEARANCE				
TYPE OF FIT				

5. H11/c11

6. H7/g6

7. N7/h6

8. H7/s6

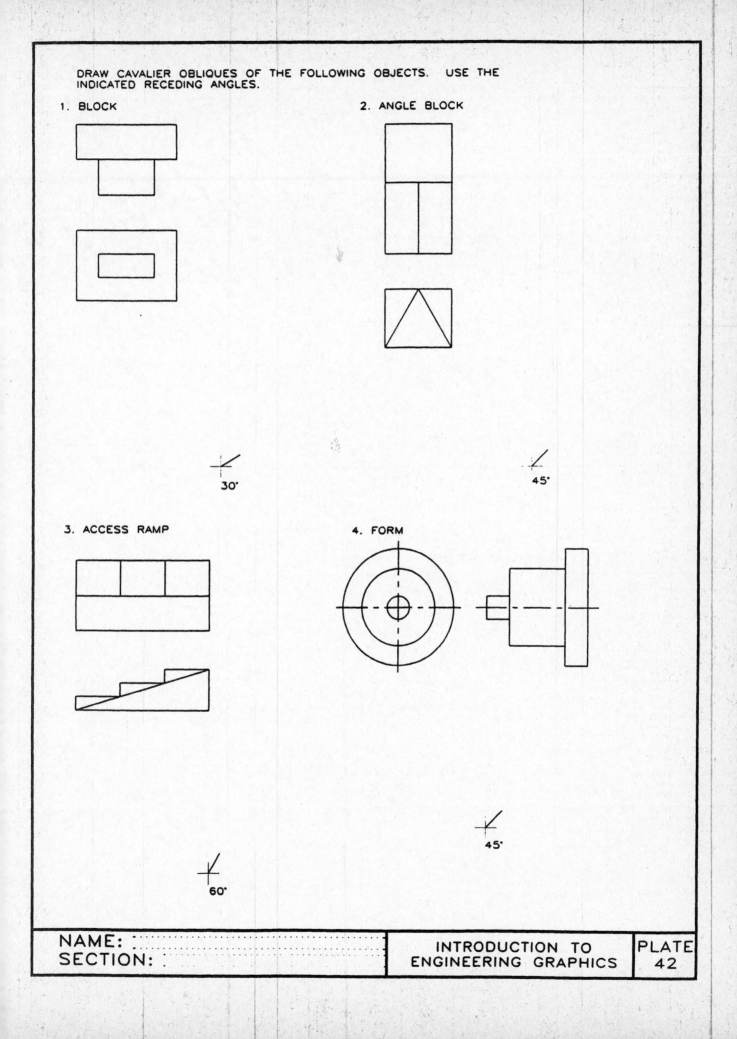

DRAW CAVALIER OBLIQUES OF THE FOLLOWING OBJECTS. USE THE
INDICATED RECEDING ANGLES.

1. BLOCK

2. ANGLE BLOCK

30°

45°

3. ACCESS RAMP

4. FORM

60°

45°

PLEASE DRAW THE DECO BOOKCASE AS
AS A CABINET AND CAVALIER OBLIQUE.
USE A RECEDING ANGLE OF 45°

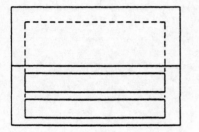

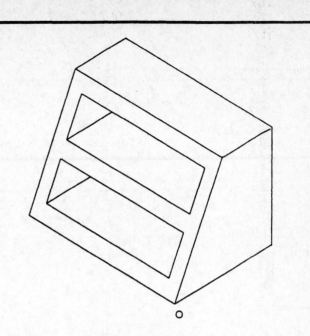

DECO BOOKCASE
CAST STONE
SCALE 1/8"=1'-0

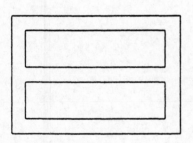

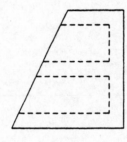

O

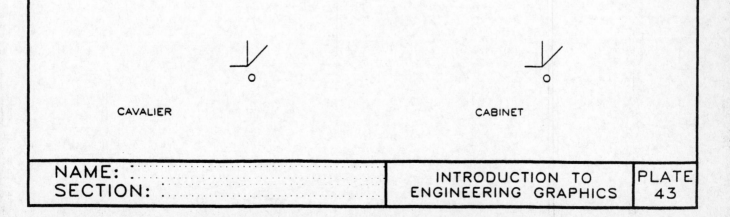

CAVALIER

CABINET

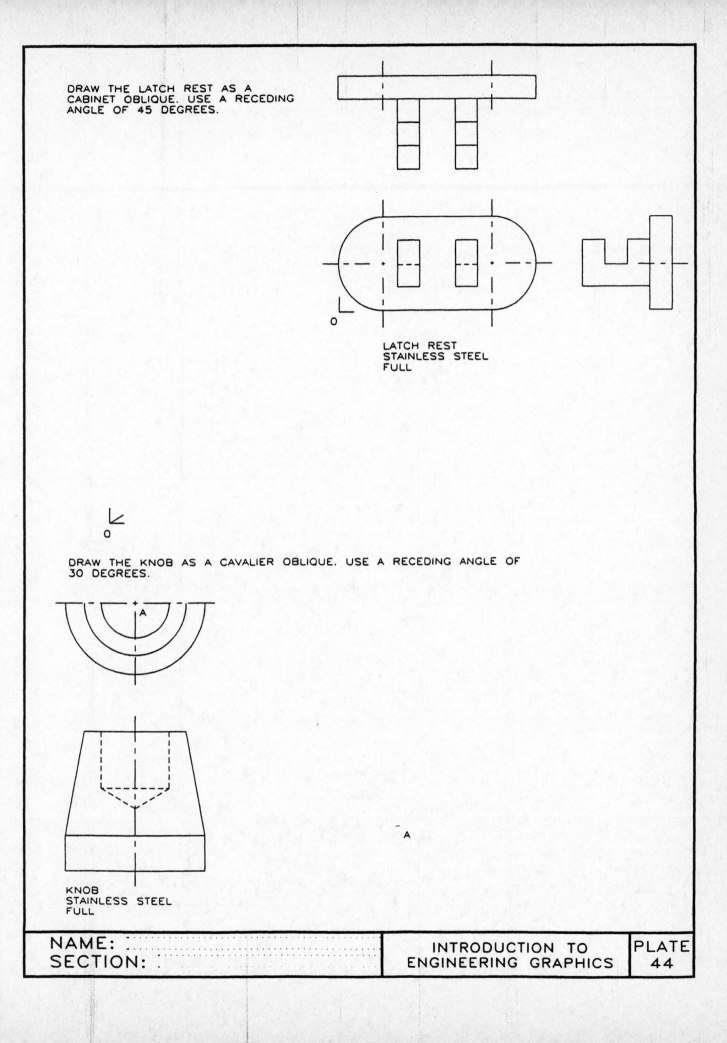

DRAW THE LATCH REST AS A
CABINET OBLIQUE. USE A RECEDING
ANGLE OF 45 DEGREES.

LATCH REST
STAINLESS STEEL
FULL

DRAW THE KNOB AS A CAVALIER OBLIQUE. USE A RECEDING ANGLE OF
30 DEGREES.

KNOB
STAINLESS STEEL
FULL

NAME:

SECTION:

INTRODUCTION TO
ENGINEERING GRAPHICS

PLATE
44

CONSTRUCT DOUBLE SIZE ISOMETRIC DRAWINGS OF EACH OF THE OBJECTS SHOWN BELOW.

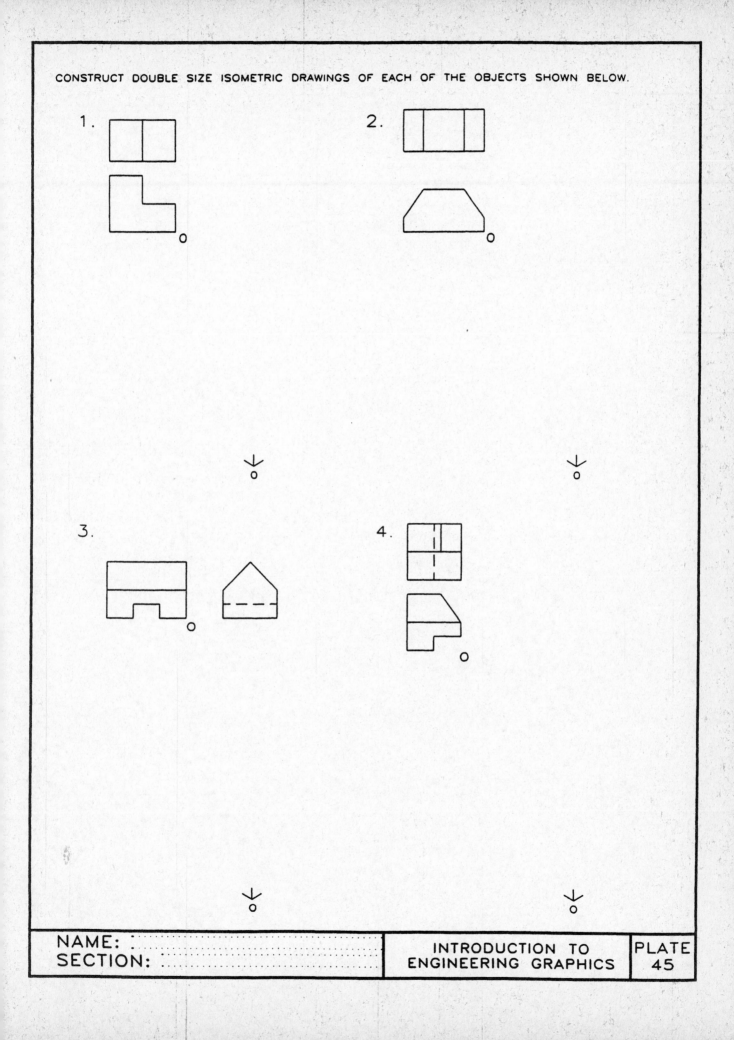

1.

2.

3.

4.

SKETCH OR CONSTRUCT THREE MULTIVIEWS FOR ALL PROBLEMS.

1.

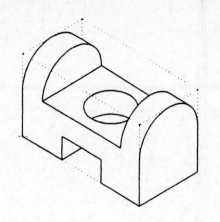

2.

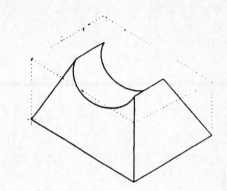

L   L

3.

4.

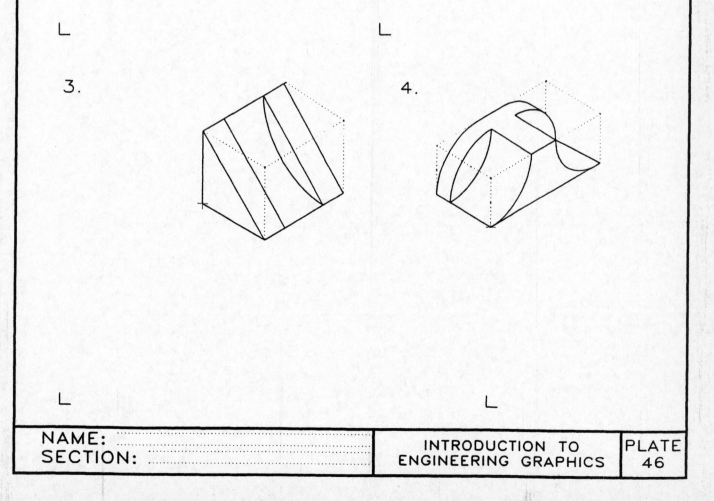

L   L

SKETCH THE FOLLOWING STAIRS AS AN ISOMETRIC ON THE GRID PROVIDED.

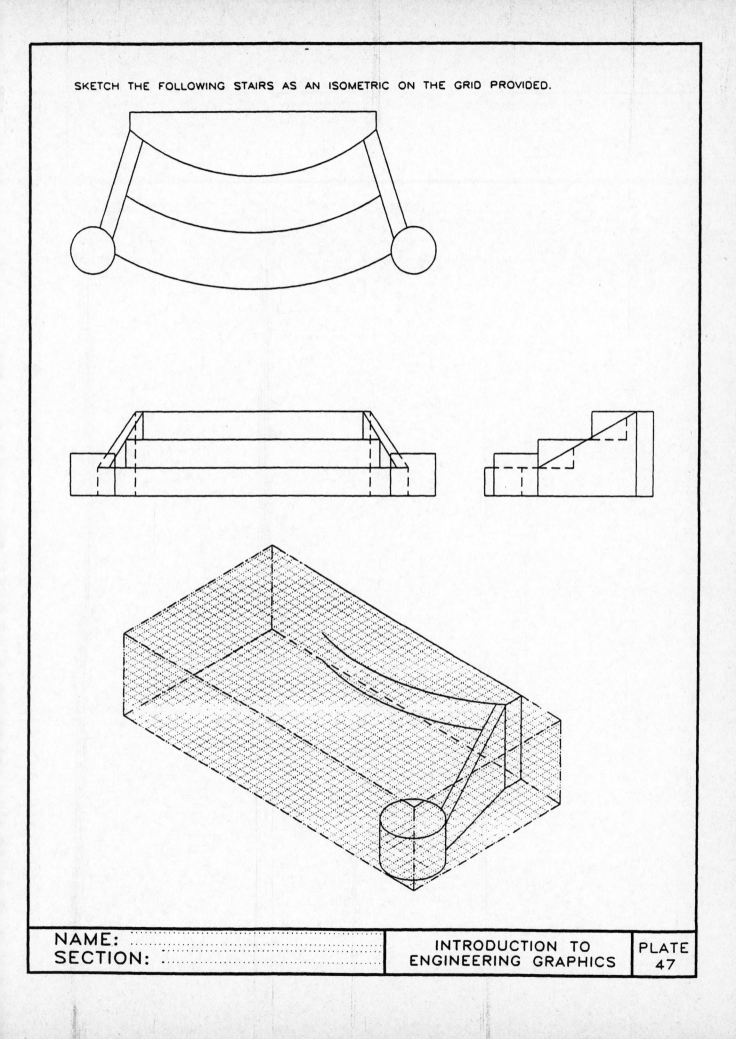

CONSTRUCT A FULL—SIZED ISOMETRIC DRAWING OF THE OBJECT SHOWN BELOW.

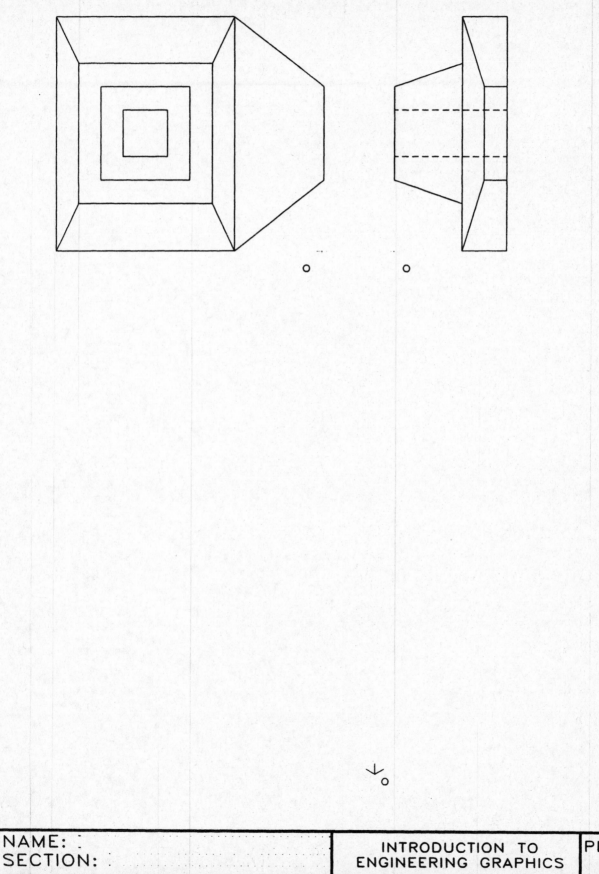

ALL OBJECTS ON THIS PAGE ARE PLASTIC AND HAVE A UNIFORM THICKNESS OF 1/16"
SKETCH THE TOP AND FRONT VIEW OF THESE OBJECTS USING A SINGLE LINE TO
REPRESENT EACH EDGE. ADD THE NEEDED HIDDEN LINES TO YOUR SKETCHES USING SINGLE
LINES FOR EACH EDGE.

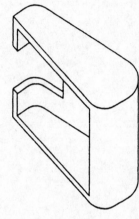

MOUSE CASE

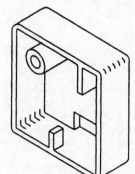

BATTERY CASE

STUDY THE DIAGRAM.

SMALL BOWL (THE MOLD; THE PART
BEING MANUFACTURED)

COLD SLUG WELL

GATE

LAYOUT DIAGRAM

SMALL BOWL
(THE PART
BEING
MANUFACTURED)

GATE
THE CHANNEL
THROUGH WHICH
THE MOLTEN MATERIAL
FLOWS INTO THE PATTERN
PIECE.

SPRUE
THE OPENING
THROUGH WHICH
MOLTEN MATERIAL
FLOWS TO THE
RUNNERS

RUNNER
THE CHANNEL FOR
CONDUCTING MOLTEN
MATERIAL TO THE
MOLD

DRAW A DIAGRAM THAT REPRESENTS THE LAYOUT OF
AN INJECTION MOLD TO MANUFACTURE EIGHT DINNER PLATES.

PLACE THESE OBJECTS SO THAT A FLAT EDGE
SO THAT IS IN CONTACT WITH THE GATE.

DRAW THE RUNNERS WITH A DIAMETER OF 1/16".
DRAW THE GATES WITH A DIAMETER OF 1/32"

THE BASIC LAYOUT IS GIVEN BELOW.

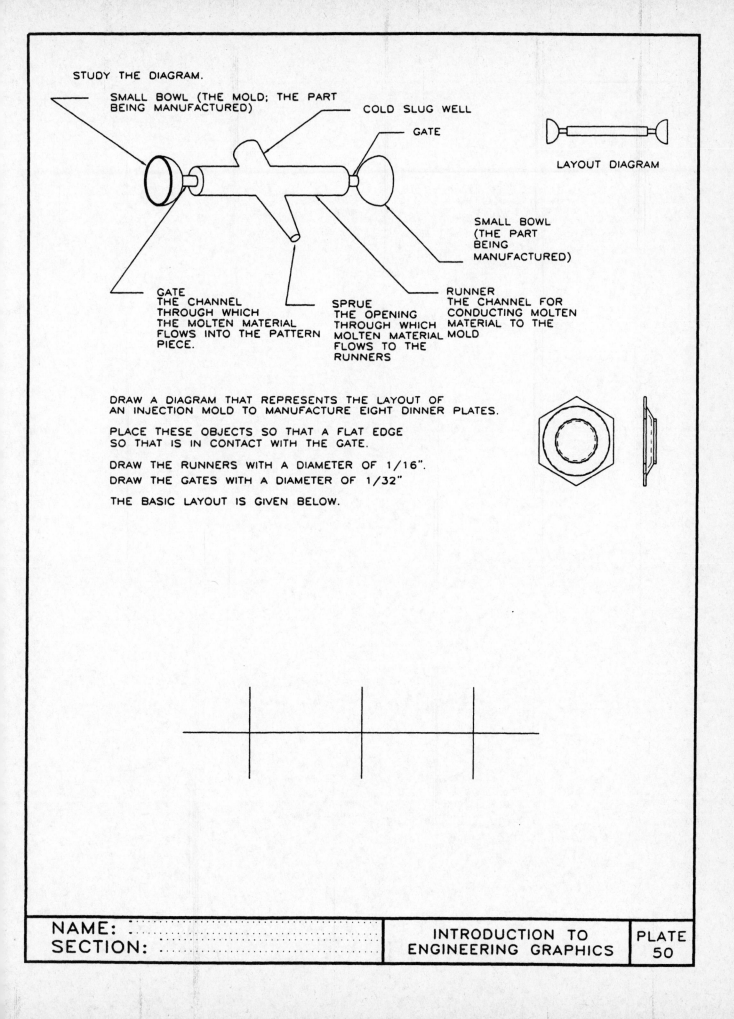

DRAW TWO VIEWS OF THE OBJECTS CREATED BY THE CAVITY MOLDS ILLUSTRATED BELOW.
ASSUME ALL PARTS ARE 2 INCHES LONG.   SKETCH THESE PARTS APPROXIMATELY
THREE TIMES THEIR FULL SIZE.

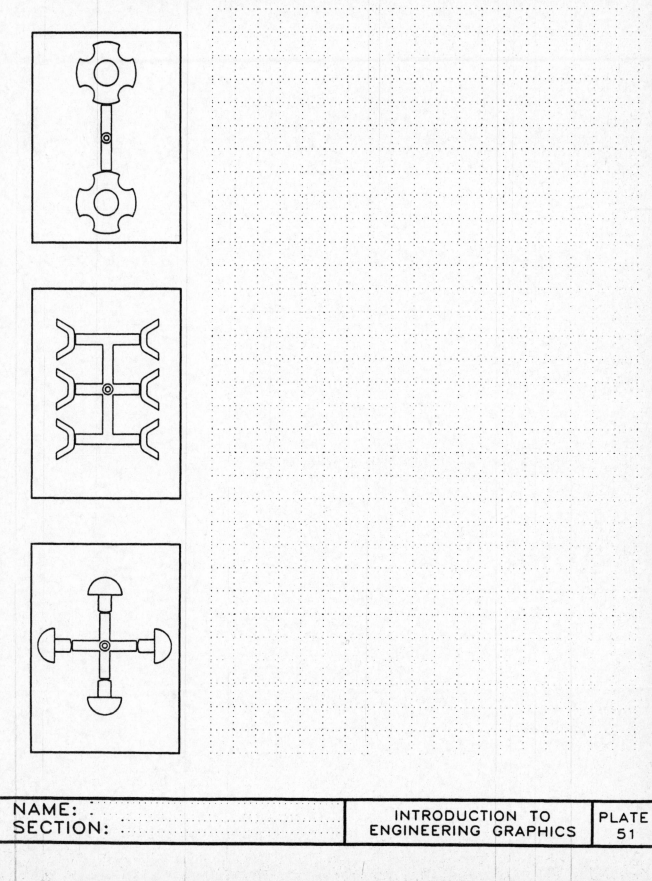

COMPUTER I INSTRUCTIONS

OPEN THE FILE COMP1.DWG.

DRAW THE FOLLOWING PATTERN FOR AN ENVELOPE FULL SCALE. USE ABSOLUTE, RELATIVE OR
POLAR COORDINATES.   DO NOT DRAW THE DIMENSIONS.   IF DRAWN CORRECTLY, YOUR DRAWING
CAN BE CUT AND FOLDED INTO AN ENVELOPE AS ILLUSTRATED IN FIGURE 1.

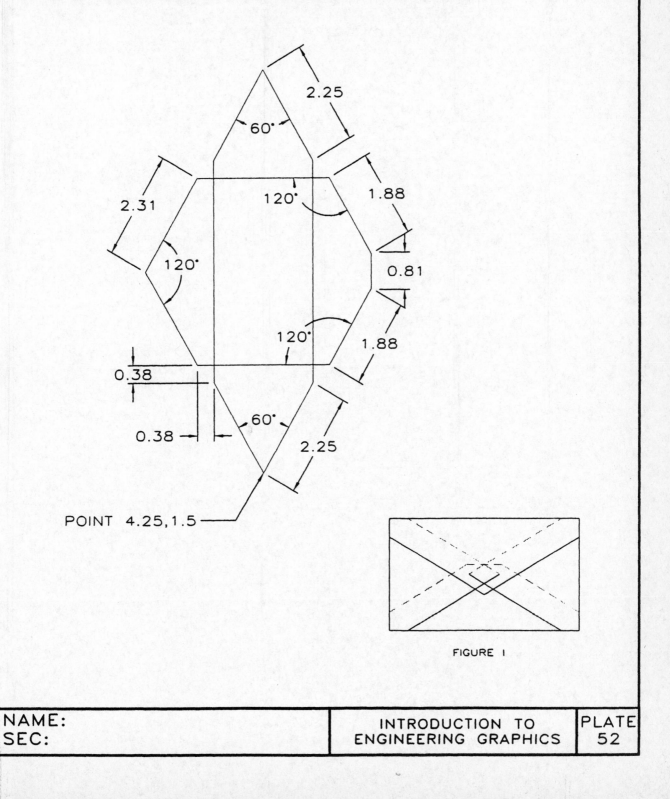

FIGURE I

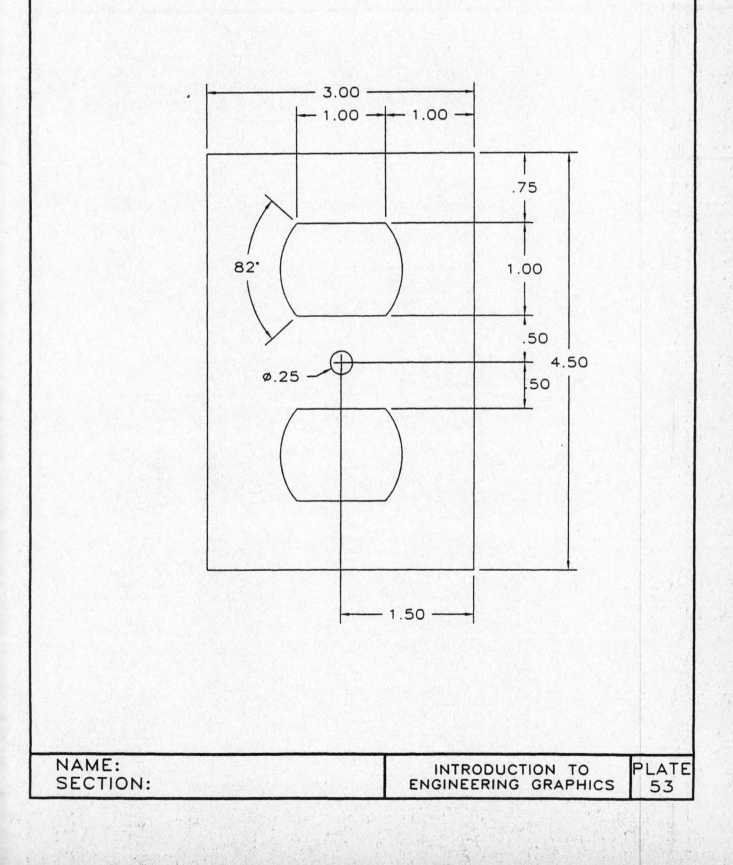

COMPUTER 3 INSTRUCTIONS

OPEN THE ACAD DRAWING FILE COMP3.DWG.
DRAW THE CHART SHOWN BELOW.

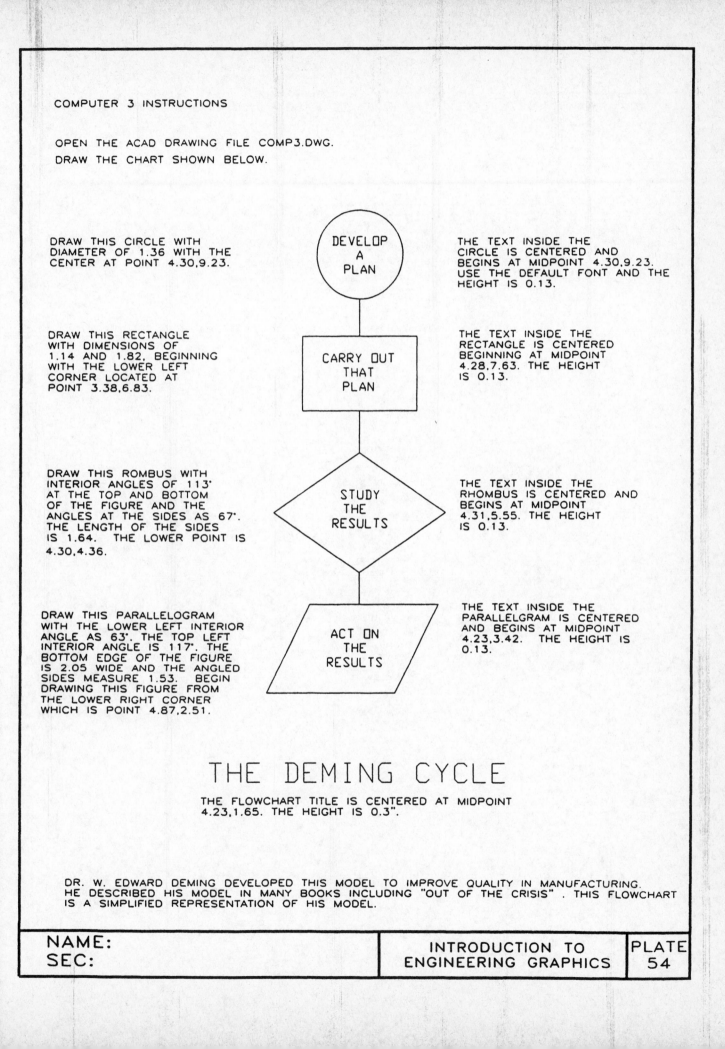

DRAW THIS CIRCLE WITH
DIAMETER OF 1.36 WITH THE
CENTER AT POINT 4.30,9.23.

DEVELOP
A
PLAN

THE TEXT INSIDE THE
CIRCLE IS CENTERED AND
BEGINS AT MIDPOINT 4.30,9.23.
USE THE DEFAULT FONT AND THE
HEIGHT IS 0.13.

DRAW THIS RECTANGLE
WITH DIMENSIONS OF
1.14 AND 1.82, BEGINNING
WITH THE LOWER LEFT
CORNER LOCATED AT
POINT 3.38,6.83.

CARRY OUT
THAT
PLAN

THE TEXT INSIDE THE
RECTANGLE IS CENTERED
BEGINNING AT MIDPOINT
4.28,7.63. THE HEIGHT
IS 0.13.

DRAW THIS ROMBUS WITH
INTERIOR ANGLES OF 113°
AT THE TOP AND BOTTOM
OF THE FIGURE AND THE
ANGLES AT THE SIDES AS 67°.
THE LENGTH OF THE SIDES
IS 1.64. THE LOWER POINT IS
4.30,4.36.

STUDY
THE
RESULTS

THE TEXT INSIDE THE
RHOMBUS IS CENTERED AND
BEGINS AT MIDPOINT
4.31,5.55. THE HEIGHT
IS 0.13.

DRAW THIS PARALLELOGRAM
WITH THE LOWER LEFT INTERIOR
ANGLE AS 63°. THE TOP LEFT
INTERIOR ANGLE IS 117°. THE
BOTTOM EDGE OF THE FIGURE
IS 2.05 WIDE AND THE ANGLED
SIDES MEASURE 1.53.   BEGIN
DRAWING THIS FIGURE FROM
THE LOWER RIGHT CORNER
WHICH IS POINT 4.87,2.51.

ACT ON
THE
RESULTS

THE TEXT INSIDE THE
PARALLELGRAM IS CENTERED
AND BEGINS AT MIDPOINT
4.23,3.42.   THE HEIGHT IS
0.13.

THE DEMING CYCLE

THE FLOWCHART TITLE IS CENTERED AT MIDPOINT
4.23,1.65. THE HEIGHT IS 0.3".

DR. W. EDWARD DEMING DEVELOPED THIS MODEL TO IMPROVE QUALITY IN MANUFACTURING.
HE DESCRIBED HIS MODEL IN MANY BOOKS INCLUDING "OUT OF THE CRISIS" . THIS FLOWCHART
IS A SIMPLIFIED REPRESENTATION OF HIS MODEL.

NAME:
SEC:

INTRODUCTION TO
ENGINEERING GRAPHICS

PLATE
54

COMPUTER 4 INSTRUCTIONS

OPEN THE ACAD DRAWING FILE COMP4.DWG.
COMPLETE THE TWO TITLE BLOCKS GIVEN THE FOLLOWING INFORMATION.

PROBLEM 1

TEXT AT	FONT	HEIGHT	ALIGNMENT	ROTATION
①	ITALIC COMPLEX	.12	CENTERED	0°
②	ROMAN DUPLEX	.18	CENTERED	0°
③	ROMAN SIMPLEX	.12	LEFT	0°
④	ROMAN SIMPLEX	.08	CENTERED	0°

PROBLEM 2

⑤	GOTHIC ENGLISH	.25	CENTERED	90°
⑥	SCRIPT SIMPLEX	.20	CENTERED	90°
⑦	ITALIC COMPLEX	.12	LEFT	90°

⑤

⑦

NAME: YOUR NAME HERE

DATE HERE   SCALE: 1:10   1/38

GOTHIC RENOVATIONS ⑥
"Dedicated to preserving our past"

PROBLEM 2

LOUISIANA STATE UNIVERSITY
BATON ROUGE, LOUISIANA ①

COMPUTER ASSIGNMENT ②

NAME: ③	SEC: ③	SCALE FULL ④
INSTRUCTOR: ③	DATE: ③	SHEET 1 OF 1 ④

PROBLEM 1

COMPUTER 5 INSTRUCTIONS

OPEN THE ACAD DRAWING FILE COMP5.DWG.

IN THE FILE WILL BE FIVE PIECES TO A PUZZLE AND THE OUTLINE FOR THE FINISHED
PUZZLE. USE MODIFY COMMANDS AND OBJECT SNAP OPTIONS TO COMPLETE THE
PUZZLE. THE SOLUTION TO THE PUZZLE IS GIVEN BELOW.

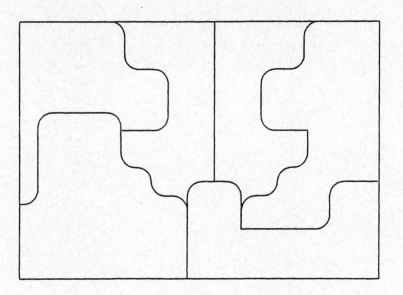

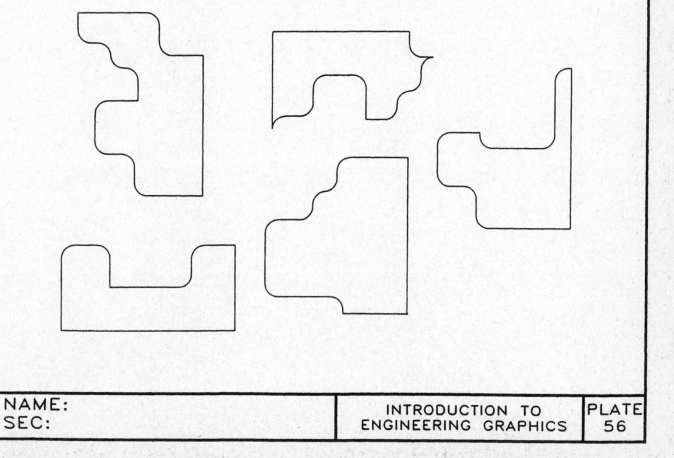

COMPUTER 6 INSTRUCTIONS

OPEN THE ACAD DRAWING FILE COMP6.DWG.

CREATE THE DESIGN GIVEN USING THE POLYGON AND OBJECT SNAP
OPTIONS. THE SMALLER WHITE CIRCLE IS GIVEN AS A STARTING POINT.
CREATE SEPERATE LAYERS FOR EACH COLOR AND LINETYPE. THE BLUE
LINES ARE CENTER LINES; THE RED LINES ARE HIDDEN LINES.

NAME:
SEC:

INTRODUCTION TO
ENGINEERING GRAPHICS

PLATE
57

COMPUTER 7

OPEN THE ACAD DRAWING FILE COMP7.DWG.

PROBLEM 1

- -DRAW A 4" DIAMETER CIRCLE
- -INSCRIBE A SQUARE WITHIN THIS CIRCLE.
- -OFFSET THE SQUARE .75" INSIDE THE FIRST SQUARE.
- -DRAW 4 ARCS WITH THEIR CENTER POINTS AT THE MIDPOINTS OF THE SQUARE AND THEIR ENDPOINTS AT THE 90° ANGLES OF THE SQUARE.
- -TRIM THE SMALL SQUARE.

PROBLEM 2

- -CONSTRUCT THE FOLLOWING OBJECT. OMIT THE DIMENSIONS.

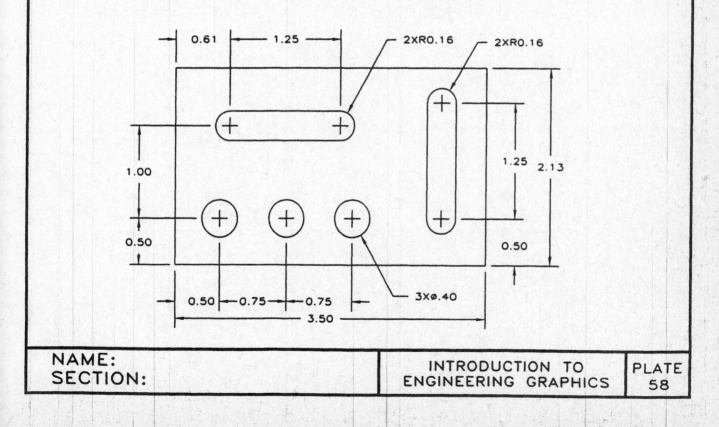

COMPUTER 8 INSTRUCTIONS

OPEN THE FILE COMP8.DWG AND COMPLETE THE PROBLEMS BELOW.

THE DRAWING BELOW IS MEANT TO REPRESENT TWO VIEWS OF A SIMPLE OBJECT.
THIS DRAWING NEEDS TO BE CORRECTED. YOU ARE TO CORRECT THIS DRAWING
USING EXTEND AND TRIM. WHEN FINISHED ADJUST THE LTSCALE SO THAT THE
DIFFERENT LINETYPES ARE BETTER REPRESENTED.

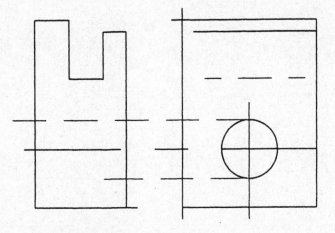

COMPLETE THE FRONT AND RIGHT SIDE VIEW OF THE OBJECT SHOWN BELOW.   THEN
CONSTRUCT A TOP VIEW FOR THE OBJECT.   STRETCH THE BASE OF THE OBJECT
SO THAT THE HEIGHT OF THE BASE AND THE SLOT IS INCREASE BY 0.30".

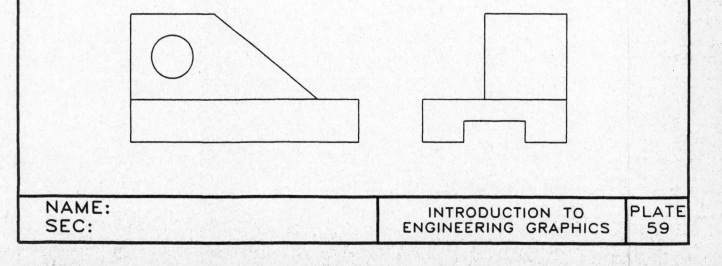

NAME:			
SEC:		INTRODUCTION TO ENGINEERING GRAPHICS	PLATE 59

COMPUTER 9 INSTRUCTIONS

OPEN THE FILE COMP9.DWG AND COMPLETE THE PROBLEMS BELOW.

PROBLEM 1

COMPLETE THE DRAWING OF THE GASKET AND ADD CENTER POINTS.   DRAW THE CENTER
POINTS OF THE CIRCLES WITH POINT.   POINT SIZE IS 1/32;   POINT TYPE IS 2.

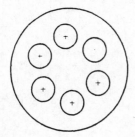 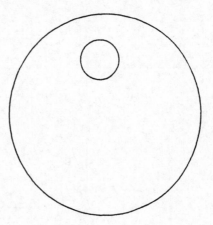

PROBLEM 2

COMPLETE THE DRAIN RACK SHOWN BELOW USING ARRAY, FILLET, PEDIT, AND OFFSET.
PLACE A .25 RADIUS FILLET AT EACH CORNER.   USE PEDIT TO JOIN THE LINES AND ARCS
INTO A POLYLINE.   USE OFFSET TO PLACE A OUTLINE COPY OF THE RACK .20 INCH AWAY.
USE THE ARRAY COMMAND TO PLACE THE HOLES.   THE HOLES ARE .50 INCH APART.

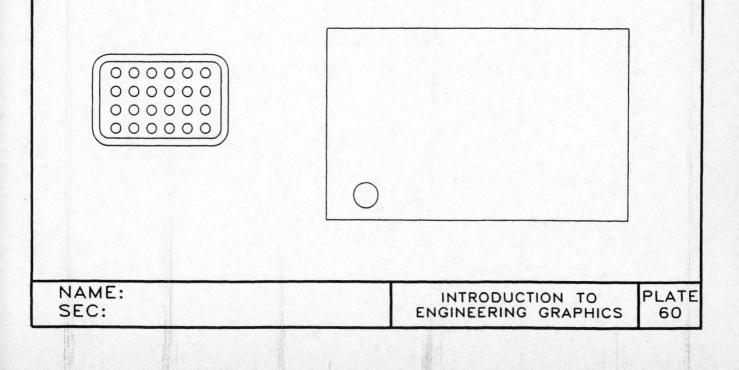

COMPUTER 10 INSTRUCTIONS

OPEN THE FILE COMP10.DWG AND DRAW THE COIN PURSE SHOWN BELOW.

CREATE A LAYER NAMED CONSTRUCTION TO PLACE THE DOTTED CIRCLES AND POLYGON
ON.   THE CONSTRUCTION LAYER SHOULD BE TURNED OFF PRIOR TO PRINTING.

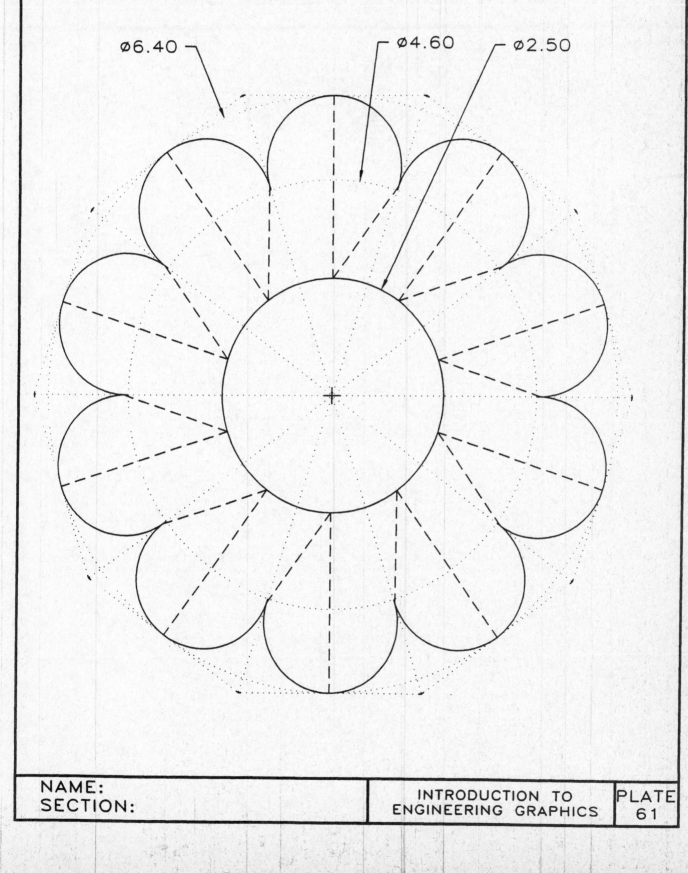

Ø6.40   Ø4.60   Ø2.50

NAME:
SECTION:

INTRODUCTION TO
ENGINEERING GRAPHICS

PLATE
61

COMPUTER 11

OPEN THE FILE COMP11.DWG AND DRAW THE FILM REEL SHOWN BELOW.
CONSTRUCT THE OBJECT AT HALF SCALE.

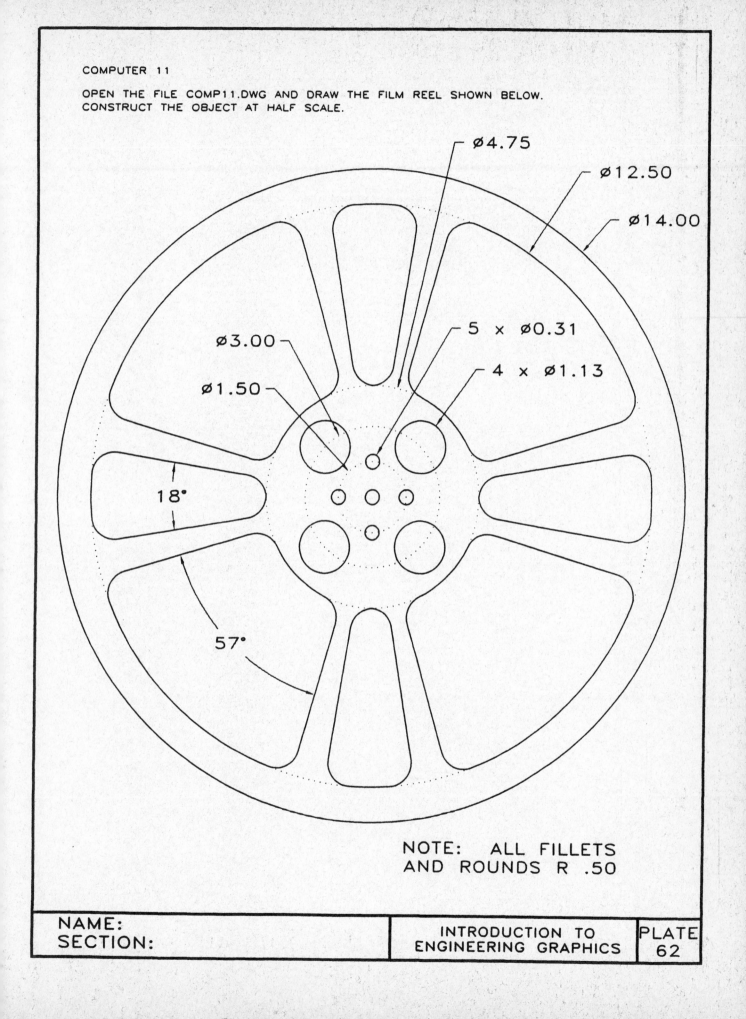

NOTE: ALL FILLETS
AND ROUNDS R .50

NAME:
SECTION:

INTRODUCTION TO
ENGINEERING GRAPHICS

PLATE
62

COMPUTER 12 INSTRUCTIONS

OPEN THE FILE COMP4.DWG AND MAKE BLOCKS OF THE TWO TITLE BLOCKS
CREATED FOR THAT ASSIGNMENT.

NAME THE BLOCKS TITLE1 AND TITLE2 TO CORRESPOND TO PROBLEM1 AND
PROBLEM2. MAKE WBLOCKS OF THE BLOCKS TITLE1 AND TITLE2. NAME THE
WBLOCKS THE SAME AS THE BLOCKS PRECEDE THE NAME WITH AN A:
TO SAVE THE WBLOCKS TO THE A: DRIVE.

NOTE: LOCATE THE INSERTION BASE POINT AS INDICATED BELOW.

LOUISIANA STATE UNIVERSITY BATON ROUGE, LOUISIANA	
COMPUTER ASSIGNMENT	
NAME: YOUR NAME HERE	SCALE FULL
INSTRUCTOR: NAME HERE.	SHEET 1 OF 1

TITLE1

TITLE2

INSERT TITLE1 INTO COMP12-1 AND REDUCE IT 25% AND ROTATE AS SHOWN.
INSERT TITLE2 INTO COMP12-2.
INSERT TITLE2 INTO COMP12-3 AND REDUCE IT 25% AND ROTATE AS SHOWN.

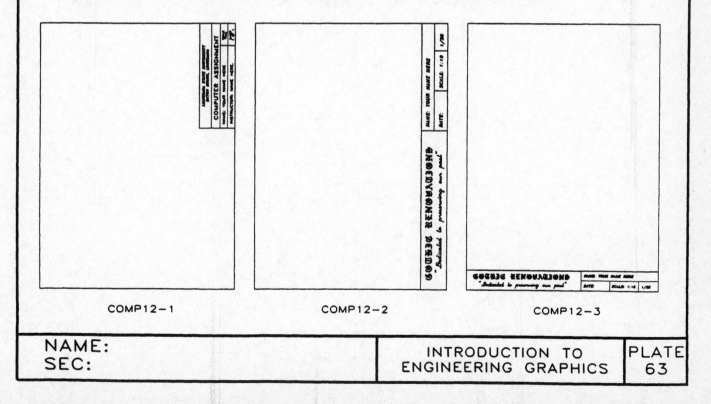

COMP12-1   COMP12-2   COMP12-3

COMPUTER 13 INSTRUCTIONS

MAKE A BLOCK OF THE ARCHED WINDOW TO THE LEFT. NAME THE BLOCK
WINDOW AND MAKE THE INSERTION BASE POINT THE LOWER LEFT CORNER
OF THE WINDOW.

INSERT THE WINDOW INTO THE CASTLE BELOW USING THE OSNAP NODE
FOR PLACEMENT. THE TOWER WINDOW NEEDS TO BE REDUCED BY 25%.
THE SIX GROUND LEVEL WINDOWS NEED TO BE ENLARGED BY 25% IN
HEIGHT ONLY.

WHEN ALL OF THE WINDOWS HAVE BEEN PLACED, MAKE A BLOCK AND
A WBLOCK OF THE CASTLE.

IF YOU NEED TO ERASE A WINDOW, TAKE CARE NOT
TO ERASE THE + LOCATION MARKS FOR EACH WINDOW.

COMPUTER 14 INSTRUCTIONS

PROBLEM 1

BEGIN A NEW DRAWING NAMED PAGEA.DWG. CREATE A SHEET SIZE OF 8.5"X11" WITH A
VERTICAL FORMAT. MAKE A 0.5" BORDER INSIDE THE PAPER EDGE. THE WIDTH OF THE
BORDER LINE IS 0.03". INSERT THE FILE TITLE2.DWG (CREATED IN COMPUTER ASSIGNMENT
12) REDUCING THE BLOCK BY 25% AND ROTATING THE BLOCK AS SHOWN BELOW. MAKE THE
APPROPRIATE TEXT CHANGES. THE FONT FOR THE TITLE IS ROMAN TRIPLEX.

COMPUTER INNOVATIONS
"THE WAVE OF THE FUTURE"

NAME: YOUR NAME HERE		
DATE HERE	SCALE: 1:10	1/38

COMPUTER INNOVATIONS
"THE WAVE OF THE FUTURE"

PROBLEM 2

BEGIN A NEW DRAWING NAMED PAGEB.DWG. CREATE AN 11"X17" SHEET SIZE. MAKE A ONE
INCH BORDER INSIDE THE PAPER EDGE. INSERT THE FILE TITLE1.DWG FULL SIZE IN THE
LOWER RIGHT CORNER. MAKE THE APPROPRIATE TEXT CHANGES.

LOUISIANA STATE UNIVERSITY INDUSTRIAL ENGINEERING	
COMPUTER GRAPHICS	
NAME: YOUR NAME HERE	SCALE FULL
PLACE DATE HERE	SHEET 1 OF 1

LOUISIANA STATE UNIVERSITY INDUSTRIAL ENGINEERING	
COMPUTER GRAPHICS	
NAME: YOUR NAME HERE	SCALE FULL
PLACE DATE HERE	SHEET 1 OF 1

NAME: SEC:	INTRODUCTION TO ENGINEERING GRAPHICS	PLATE 65

COMPUTER 15 INSTRUCTIONS

OPEN THE ACAD FILE A:COMP15.DWG.

WHEN COMPLETED YOUR DRAWING WILL BE
A LARGER DRAWING OF THE ILLUSTRATION
AT THE RIGHT.

INSERT THE CASTLE CREATED IN
COMPUTER ASSIGNMENT 13.   INSERT THIS
FILE FULL SIZE AND TO THE SIDE OF THE
PAGE ON THE RIGHT OF THE SCREEN.
YOUR SCREEN WILL LOOK LIKE THE FIGURE
TO THE RIGHT.

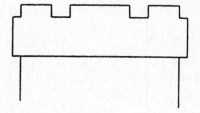

EXPLODE THE CASTLE THAT YOU JUST
INSERTED AND PLACE A ZOOM WINDOW AROUND
THE TOP OF THE TOWER.   YOUR SCREEN WILL
LOOK LIKE THE FIGURE TO THE RIGHT.

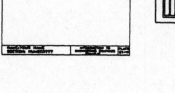

SET THE FILLET RADIUS TO 1/32".   SET THE
CHAMFER DISTANCES TO 1/16".   MODIFY THE
TOWER AS SHOWN.   TRIM OR ERASE ANY STRAY
MARKS.

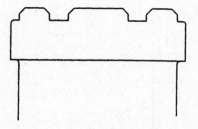

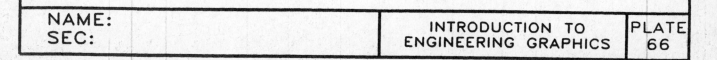

| NAME:
SEC: | INTRODUCTION TO
ENGINEERING GRAPHICS | PLATE
66 |

COMPUTER 15 INSTRUCTIONS, CONTINUED

WHEN YOU ARE FINISHED WITH THE TOWER, USE PAN SO YOU CAN SEE THE ENTIRE
DRAWING. MIRROR THE DRAWING USING THE RIGHT EDGE OF THE DRAWING AS THE
MIRROR EDGE. YOUR DRAWING SHOULD LOOK LIKE THIS:

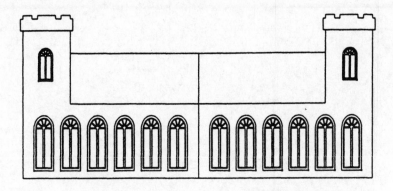

MAKE A COPY OF THE LEFT TOWER. YOUR SELECTION SET SHOULD LOOK LIKE THIS:

POINT B

POINT A

PLACE THIS COPY SO THAT IT IS ALIGNED WITH THE INTERSECTION
FORMED BY THE MIRROR LINE EDGE (POINT C) AND THE ENDPOINT OF
THE LEFT SIDE OF THE COPY (POINT A).

PLACE A SECOND COPY OF THE SAME TOWER SO THAT IT IS
ALIGNED WITH POINT C AND THE ENDPOINT OF RIGHT SIDE OF THE
COPY (POINT B).

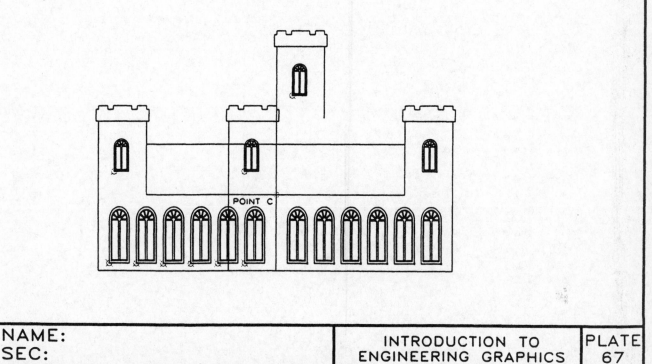

POINT C

NAME:
SEC:

INTRODUCTION TO
ENGINEERING GRAPHICS

PLATE
67

COMPUTER 15 INSTRUCTIONS, CONTINUED

USE TRIM, EXTEND, AND ERASE TO CLEAN—UP THE CASTLE SO THAT IT WILL LOOK LIKE
THE FIGURE BELOW.

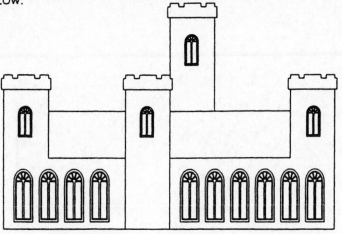

STRECH THE LEFT TOWER SO THAT IT IS TALLER BY 1/2 OF AN INCH.   USE A
WINDOW AND BE CAREFUL TO SELECT ONLY THE TOP OF THE TOWER.

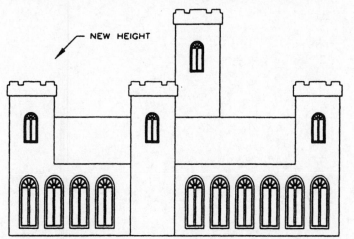

NEW HEIGHT

THE BASIC DRAWING IS NOW COMPLETE.   REDUCE THE SCALE OF THE OF DRAWING BY
50 PERCENT AND MOVE THE DRAWING INSIDE THE PAPER BORDER AND SAVE THE FILE.

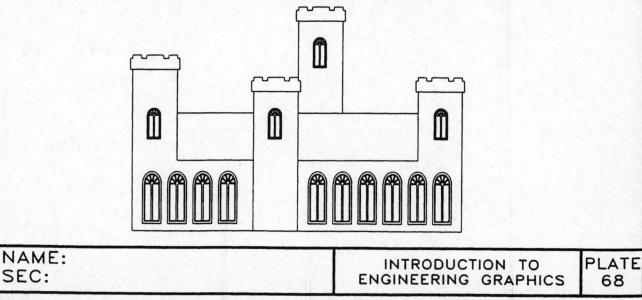

NAME:
SEC:

INTRODUCTION TO
ENGINEERING GRAPHICS

PLATE
68

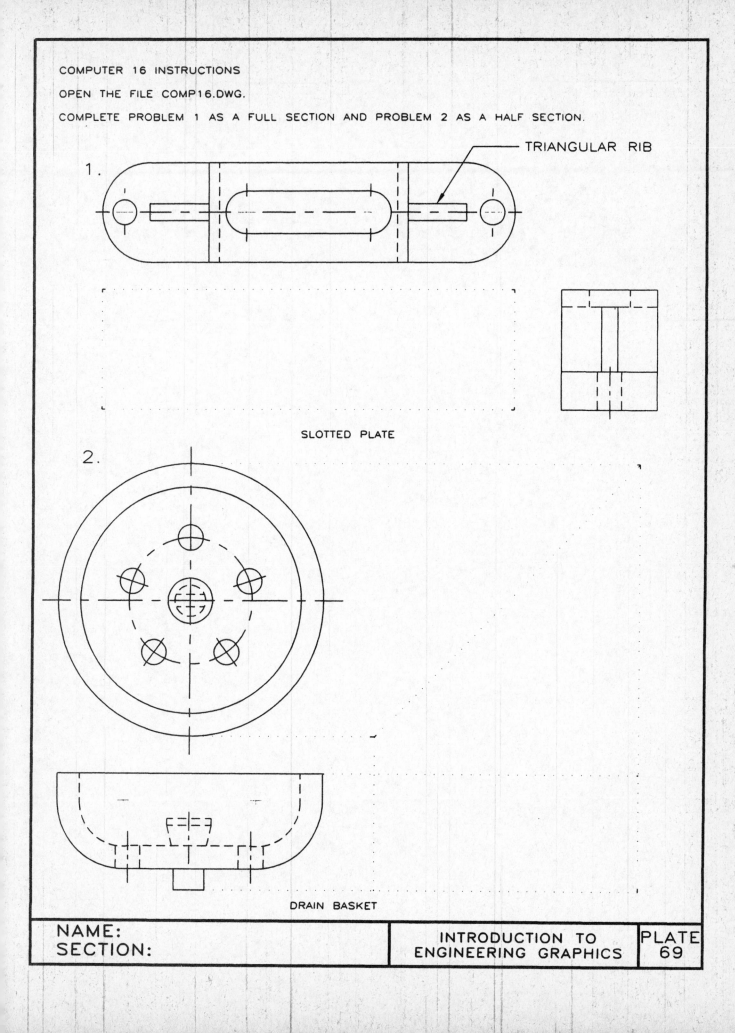

COMPUTER 16 INSTRUCTIONS

OPEN THE FILE COMP16.DWG.

COMPLETE PROBLEM 1 AS A FULL SECTION AND PROBLEM 2 AS A HALF SECTION.

1.

TRIANGULAR RIB

SLOTTED PLATE

2.

DRAIN BASKET

NAME:
SECTION:

INTRODUCTION TO
ENGINEERING GRAPHICS

PLATE
69

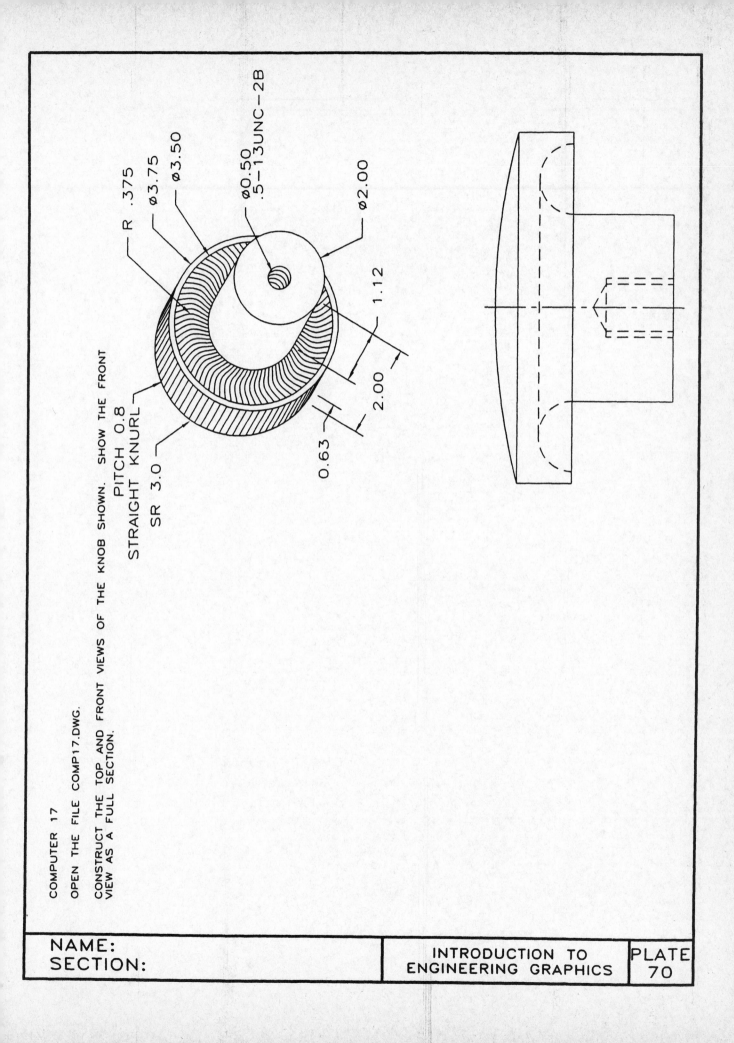

COMPUTER 17

OPEN THE FILE COMP17.DWG.

CONSTRUCT THE TOP AND FRONT VIEWS OF THE KNOB SHOWN. SHOW THE FRONT
VIEW AS A FULL SECTION.

R .375
Ø3.75
Ø3.50
Ø0.50
.5-13UNC-2B
Ø2.00
PITCH 0.8
STRAIGHT KNURL
SR 3.0
1.12
2.00
0.63

COMPUTER 18 INSTRUCTIONS

DRAW THE INIDICATED SECTION OF THE KAISER ROLL CUTTER.

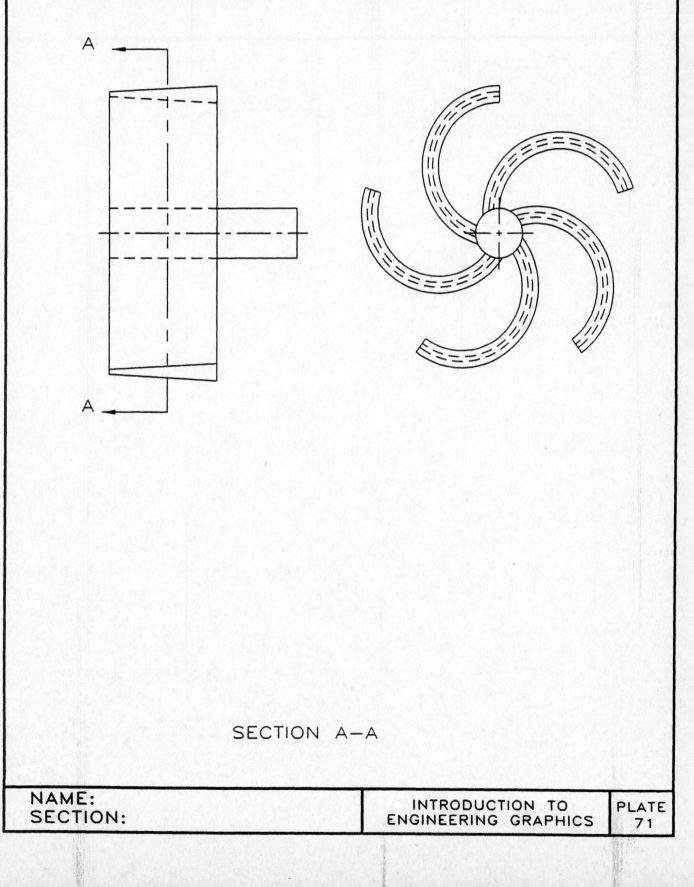

SECTION A—A

COMPUTER 19 INSTRUCTIONS

DRAW THE REMOVED SECTIONS A-A, B-B AND C-C. HATCH THESE SECTIONS
USING THE HATCH PATTERN FOR CAST IRON.   SECTION A-A IS A SQUARE.
SECTION B-B IS A REG HEX SOCKET IN A CYLINDER. SECTION C-C IS A CIRCLE.

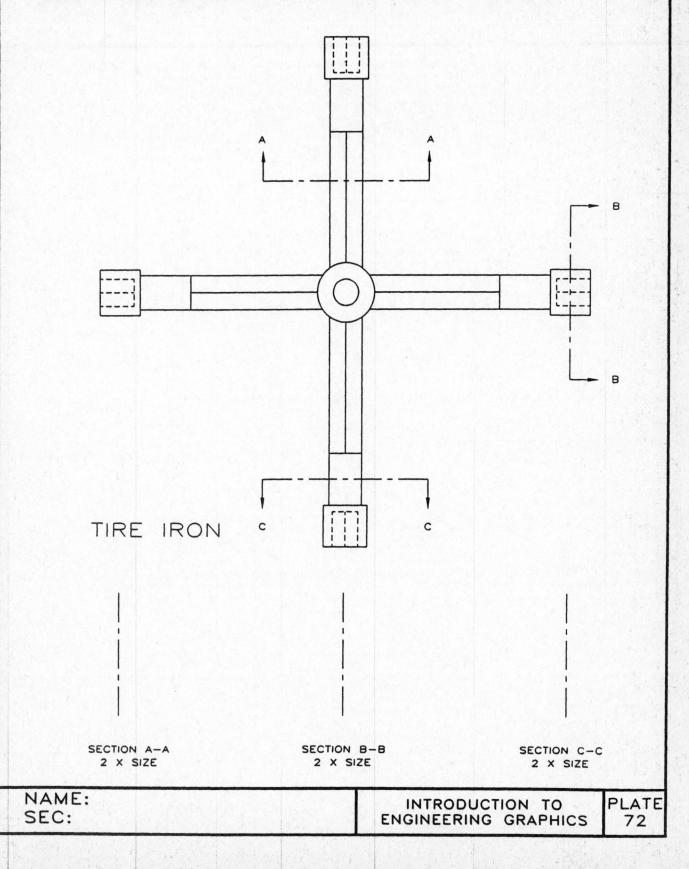

TIRE IRON

SECTION A-A
2 X SIZE

SECTION B-B
2 X SIZE

SECTION C-C
2 X SIZE

NAME:
SEC:

INTRODUCTION TO
ENGINEERING GRAPHICS

PLATE
72

OPEN THE FILE COMP20.DWG.
COMPLETE THE SECTIONED ASSEMBLY OF THE TAPE HOLDER. PARTS 1 AND 5 ARE OUTLINED BELOW.

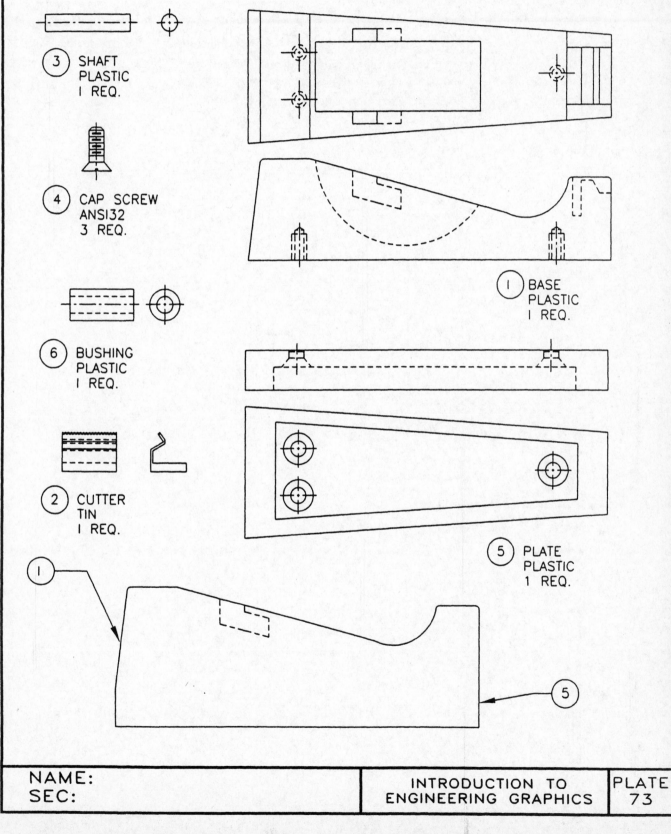

3 SHAFT
PLASTIC
1 REQ.

4 CAP SCREW
ANSI32
3 REQ.

6 BUSHING
PLASTIC
1 REQ.

2 CUTTER
TIN
1 REQ.

1 BASE
PLASTIC
1 REQ.

5 PLATE
PLASTIC
1 REQ.

NAME: SEC:		INTRODUCTION TO ENGINEERING GRAPHICS	PLATE 73

COMPUTER 21

DIMENSION THE FOLLOWING THE OBJECTS.

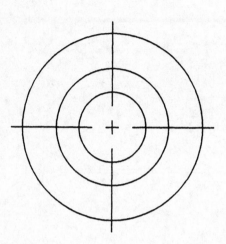
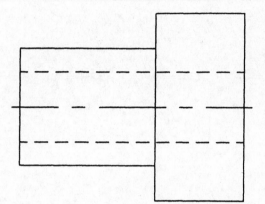

SPACER

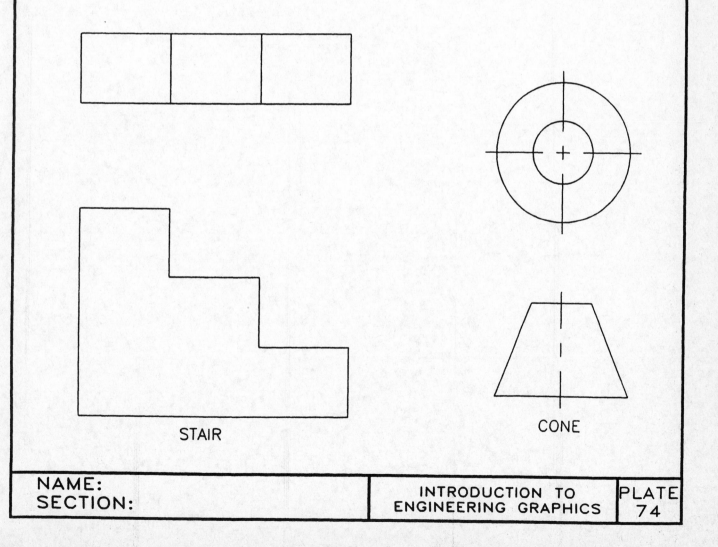

STAIR

CONE

COMPUTER 22 INSTRUCTIONS

OPEN THE FILE COMP22.DWG.

DIMENSION THE OBJECT BELOW. INCLUDE MACHINED HOLE NOTES, A ROUND NOTE, AND THE
LOCATION DIMENSIONS. THE SCALE OF THE DRAWING IS 1:1 MILLIMETERS.

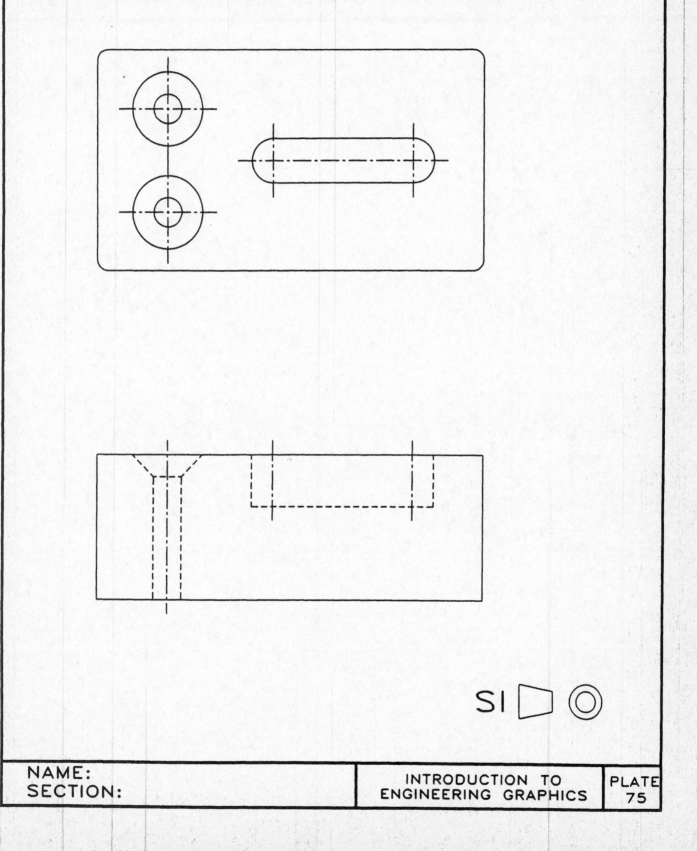

SI

COMPUTER 23 INSTRUCTIONS

OPEN THE FILE COMP23.DWG.

COMPLETELY DIMENSION THE OBJECT SHOWN BELOW.

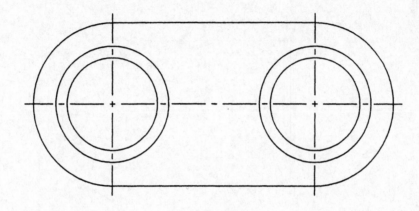

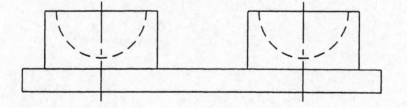

CONTACT LENSE CASE
PLASTIC
DOUBLE SIZE

COMPUTER 24 INSTRUCTIONS

OPEN THE FILE COMP24.DWG.

DIMENSION THE DOOR STOP USING THE SCALE GIVEN.

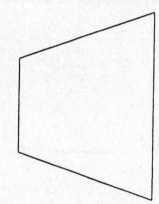

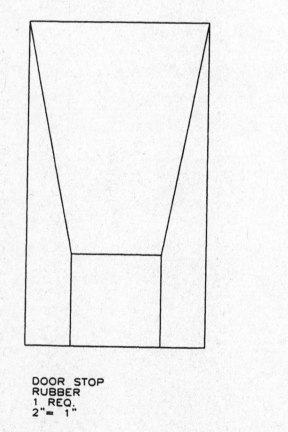

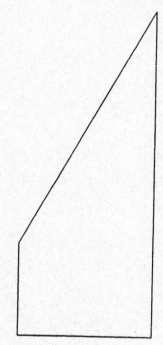

DOOR STOP
RUBBER
1 REQ.
2"= 1"

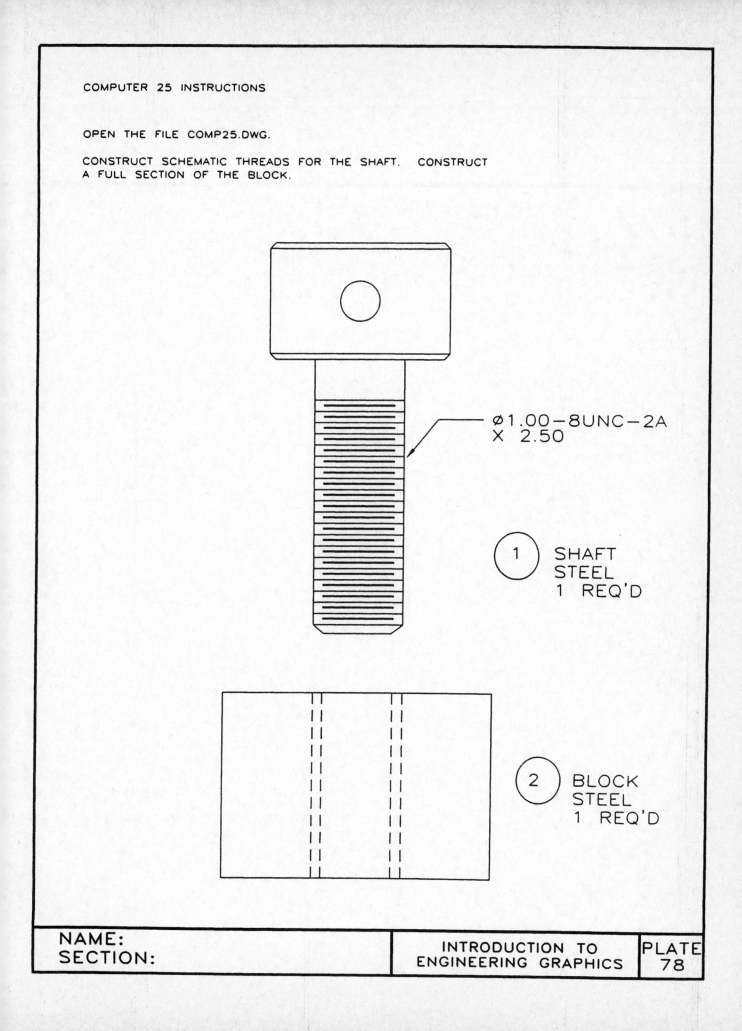

COMPUTER 25 INSTRUCTIONS

OPEN THE FILE COMP25.DWG.

CONSTRUCT SCHEMATIC THREADS FOR THE SHAFT. CONSTRUCT
A FULL SECTION OF THE BLOCK.

Ø1.00−8UNC−2A
X 2.50

1 SHAFT
   STEEL
   1 REQ'D

2 BLOCK
   STEEL
   1 REQ'D

NAME:
SECTION:

INTRODUCTION TO
ENGINEERING GRAPHICS

PLATE
78

COMPUTER 26

CREATE AN ISOMETRIC DRAWING OF THE HOUSE SHOWN BELOW. ADD ANY
FEATURES SUCH AS DOORS, WINDOWS, FIRPLACES. BESURE TO ADD SOME HATCH
PATTERNS.

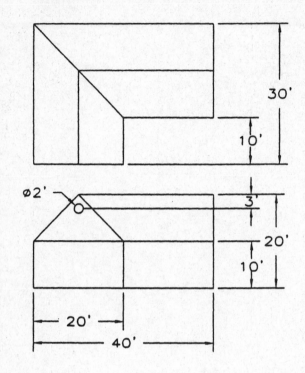

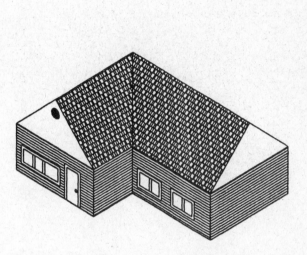

SCALE 1"=10'

NAME:
SECTION:

INTRODUCTION TO
ENGINEERING GRAPHICS

PLATE
79

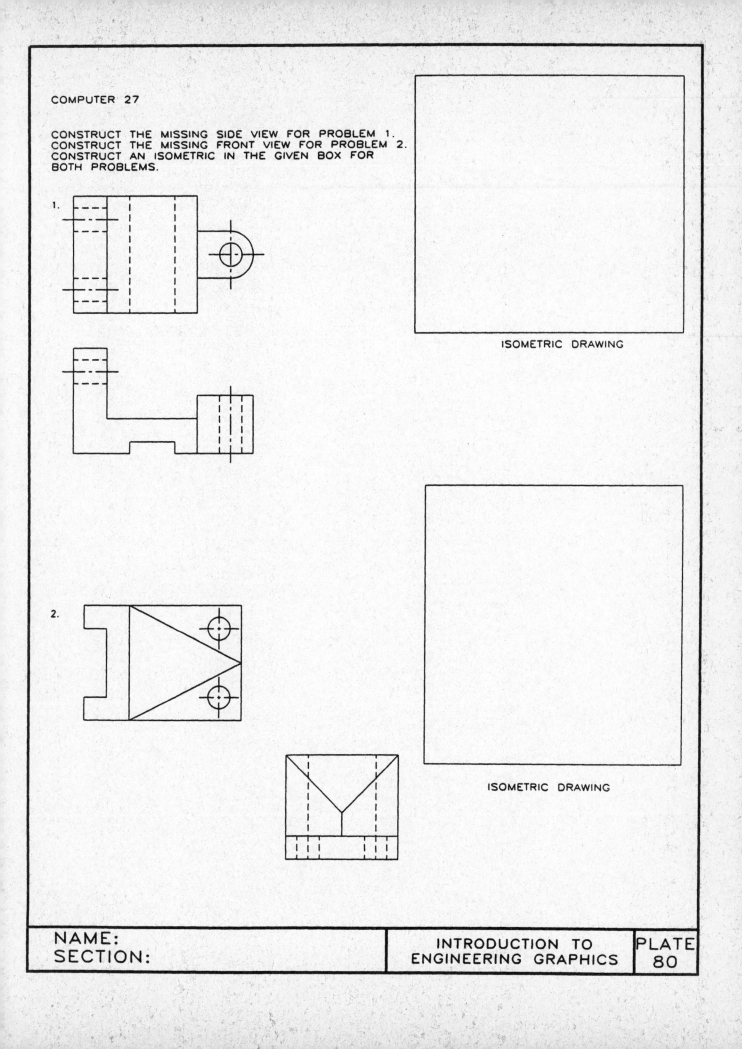

COMPUTER 27

CONSTRUCT THE MISSING SIDE VIEW FOR PROBLEM 1.
CONSTRUCT THE MISSING FRONT VIEW FOR PROBLEM 2.
CONSTRUCT AN ISOMETRIC IN THE GIVEN BOX FOR
BOTH PROBLEMS.

1.

ISOMETRIC DRAWING

2.

ISOMETRIC DRAWING

NAME:
SECTION:

INTRODUCTION TO
ENGINEERING GRAPHICS

PLATE
80

DRAW A SET OF WORKING DRAWINGS OF THE
FIRE IRON USING THE FOLLOWING INFORMATION.
PLEASE NOTE THAT THESE DRAWINGS ARE NOT
TO SCALE.

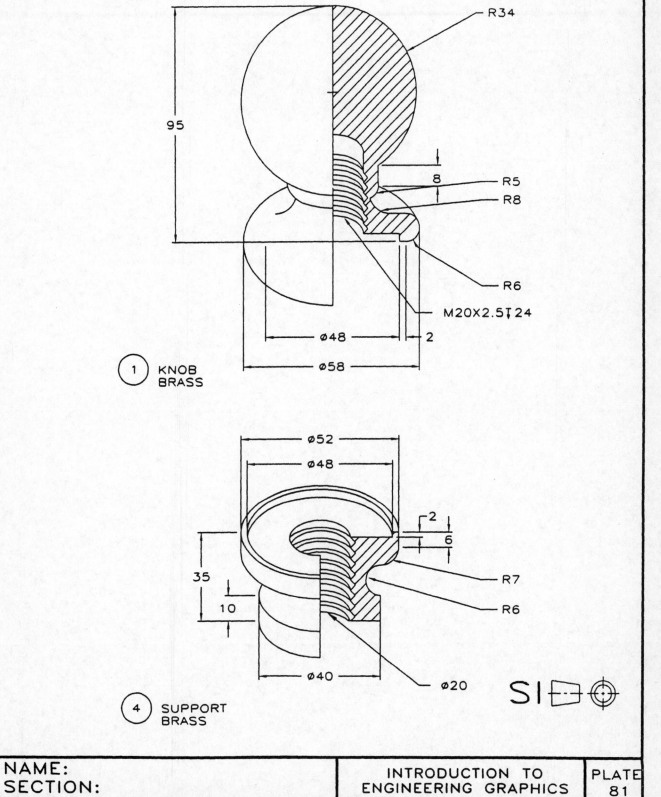

R34

95

8

R5

R8

R6

M20X2.5↧24

Ø48

2

Ø58

(1) KNOB
BRASS

Ø52

Ø48

2

6

R7

R6

35

10

Ø40

Ø20

SI

(4) SUPPORT
BRASS

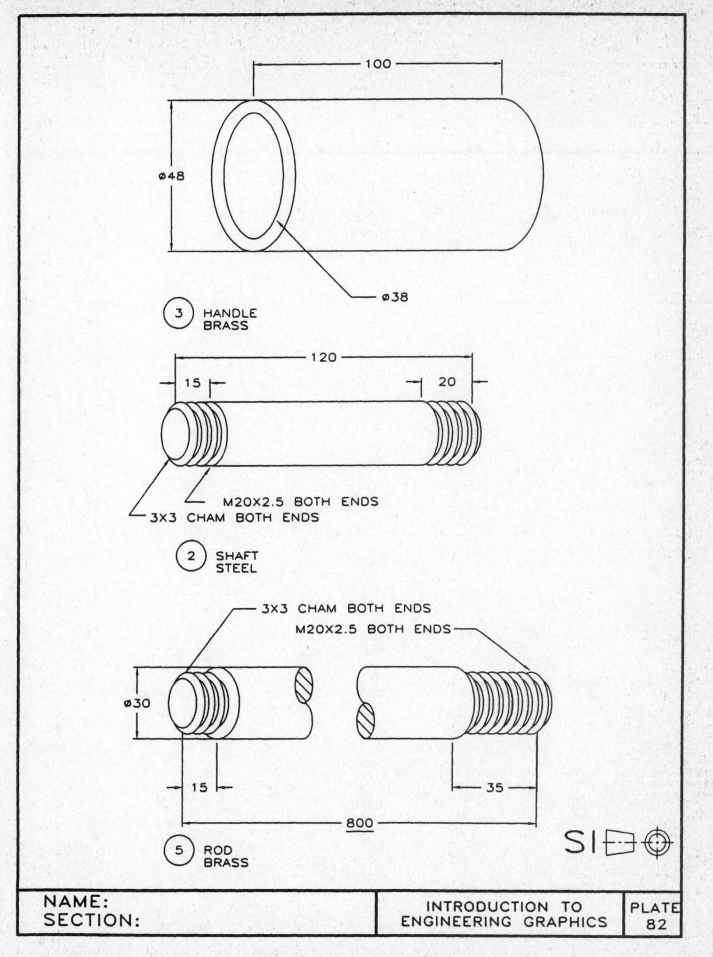

100

∅48

∅38

③ HANDLE
BRASS

120

15   20

M20X2.5 BOTH ENDS
3X3 CHAM BOTH ENDS

② SHAFT
STEEL

3X3 CHAM BOTH ENDS
M20X2.5 BOTH ENDS

∅30

15   35

800

⑤ ROD
BRASS

SI

NAME:
SECTION:

INTRODUCTION TO
ENGINEERING GRAPHICS

PLATE
82

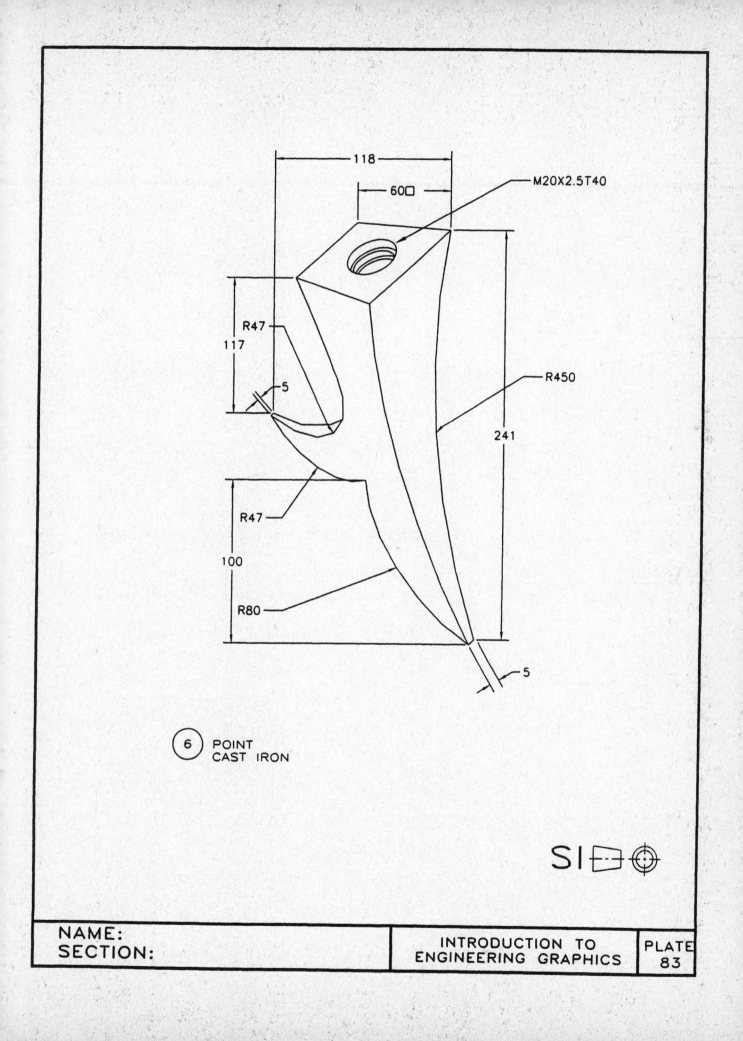

118

60☐

M20X2.5T40

R47

117

5

R450

241

R47

100

R80

5

6 POINT
CAST IRON

SI ⬠ ⊕

NAME:
SECTION:

INTRODUCTION TO
ENGINEERING GRAPHICS

PLATE
83

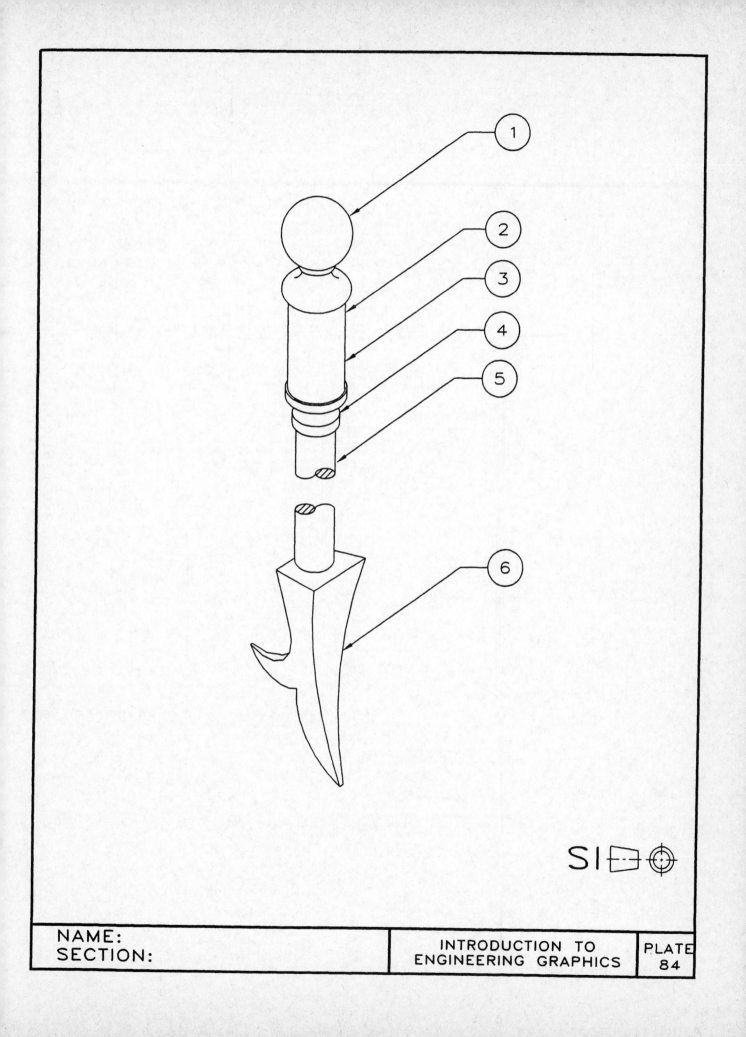

SI

NAME:
SECTION:

INTRODUCTION TO
ENGINEERING GRAPHICS

PLATE
84

COMPUTER 28 INSTRUCTIONS

OPEN THE FILE COMP28.DWG.

THE FOLLOWING DIAGRAMS ILLUSTRATE A DESIGN FOR A GATE LOCK.
IT HAS SEVERAL PARTS. ALTHOUGH THESE DIAGRAMS ILLUSTRATE THE
BASIC DESIGN, NEEDED INFORMATION IS MISSING.

CREATE A SET OF WORKING DRAWINGS AND FILL IN THE MISSING DETAILS OF
THIS DESIGN AS YOU SEE FIT. BE SURE TO MODIFY THE LOCK SO THAT IT
COULD BE ATTACHED TO A GATE. INCLUDE A LIST OF ANY STANDARD PARTS
THAT ARE USED.

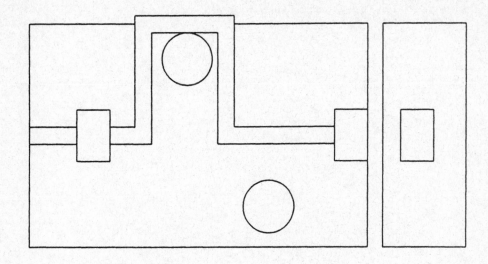

DIAGRAM 1. ILLUSTRATES THE GATE LOCK WHEN IT IS UNLOCKED.

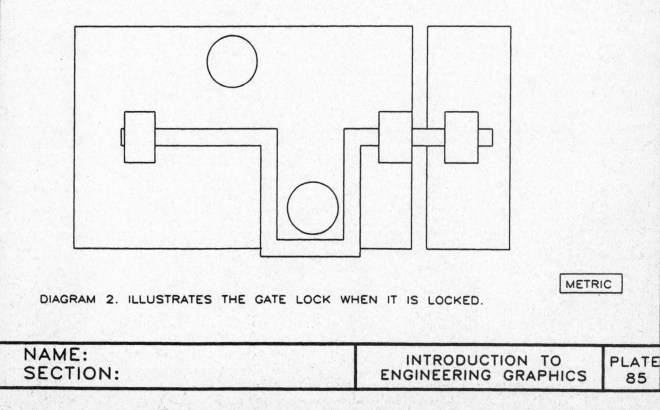

METRIC

DIAGRAM 2. ILLUSTRATES THE GATE LOCK WHEN IT IS LOCKED.

| NAME:
SECTION: | INTRODUCTION TO
ENGINEERING GRAPHICS | PLATE
85 |

NAME:
SECTION:

INTRODUCTION TO
ENGINEERING GRAPHICS

NAME:
SECTION:

INTRODUCTION TO
ENGINEERING GRAPHICS

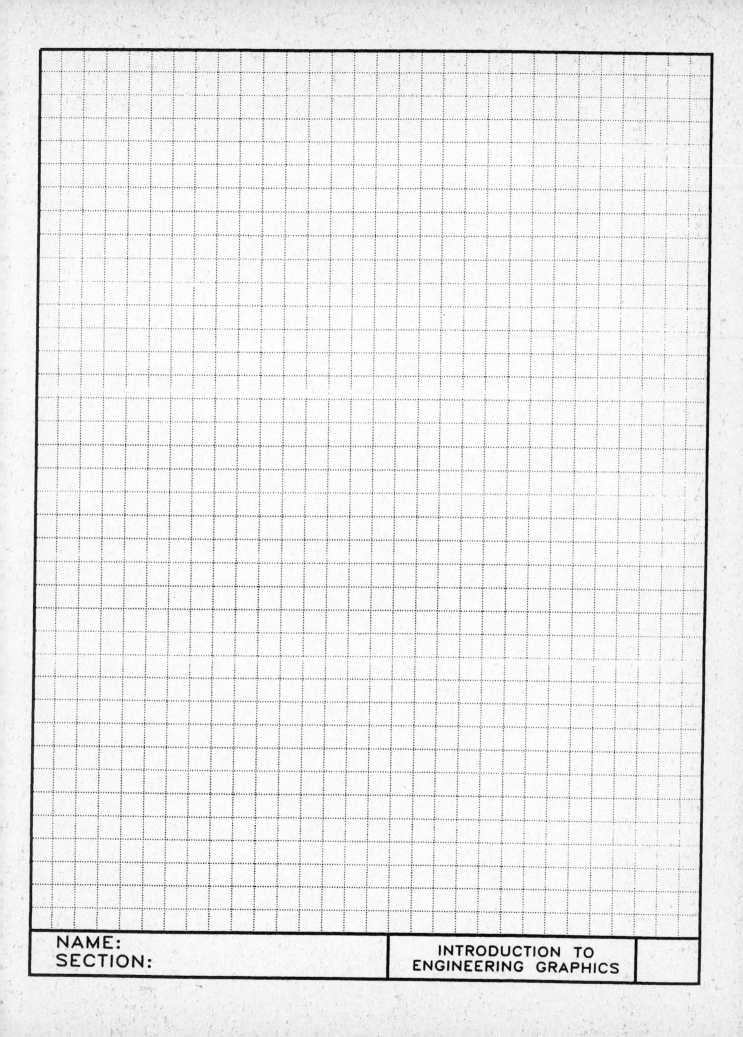

NAME:
SECTION:

INTRODUCTION TO
ENGINEERING GRAPHICS

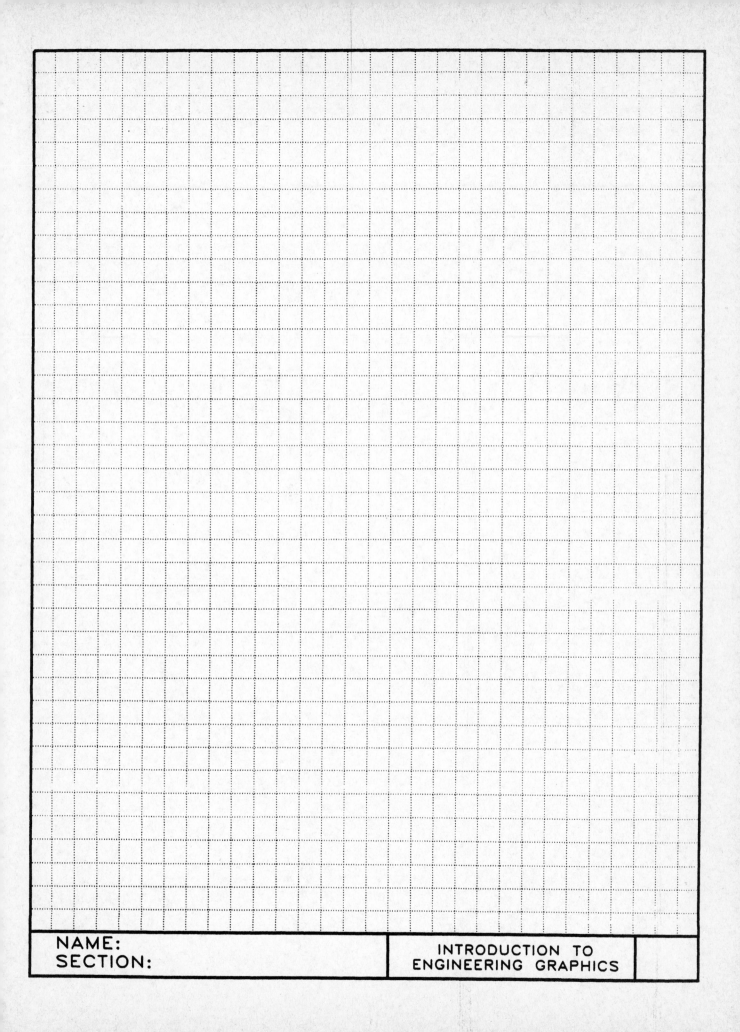

NAME:
SECTION:

INTRODUCTION TO
ENGINEERING GRAPHICS

NAME:
SECTION:

INTRODUCTION TO
ENGINEERING GRAPHICS

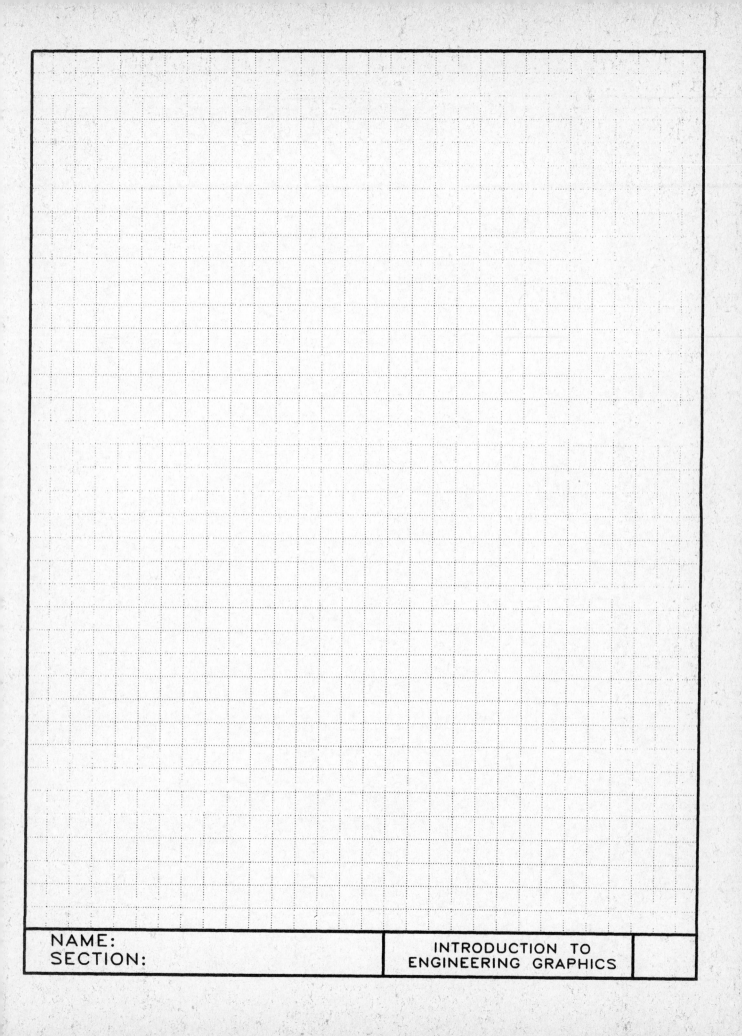

NAME:
SECTION:

INTRODUCTION TO
ENGINEERING GRAPHICS

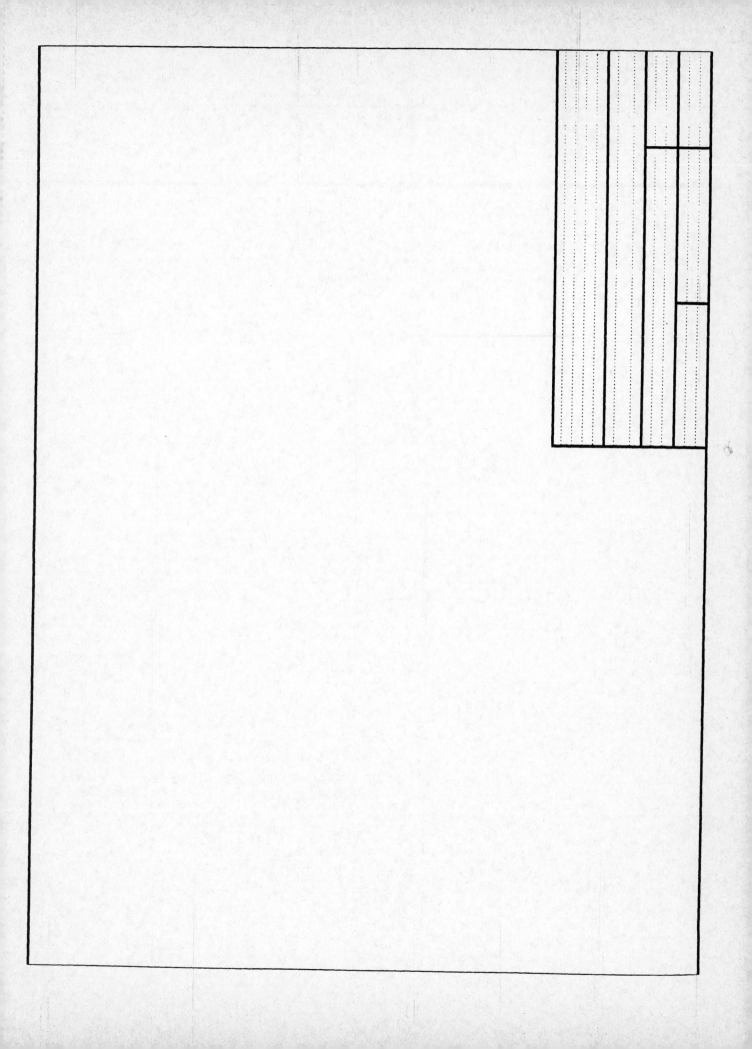

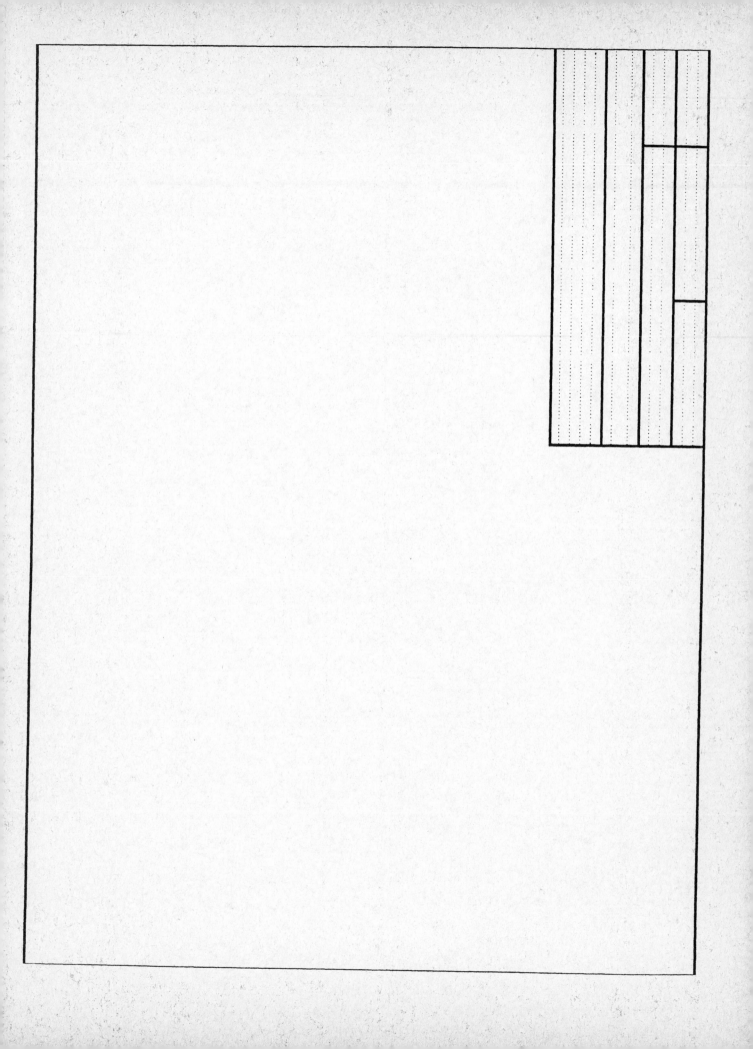

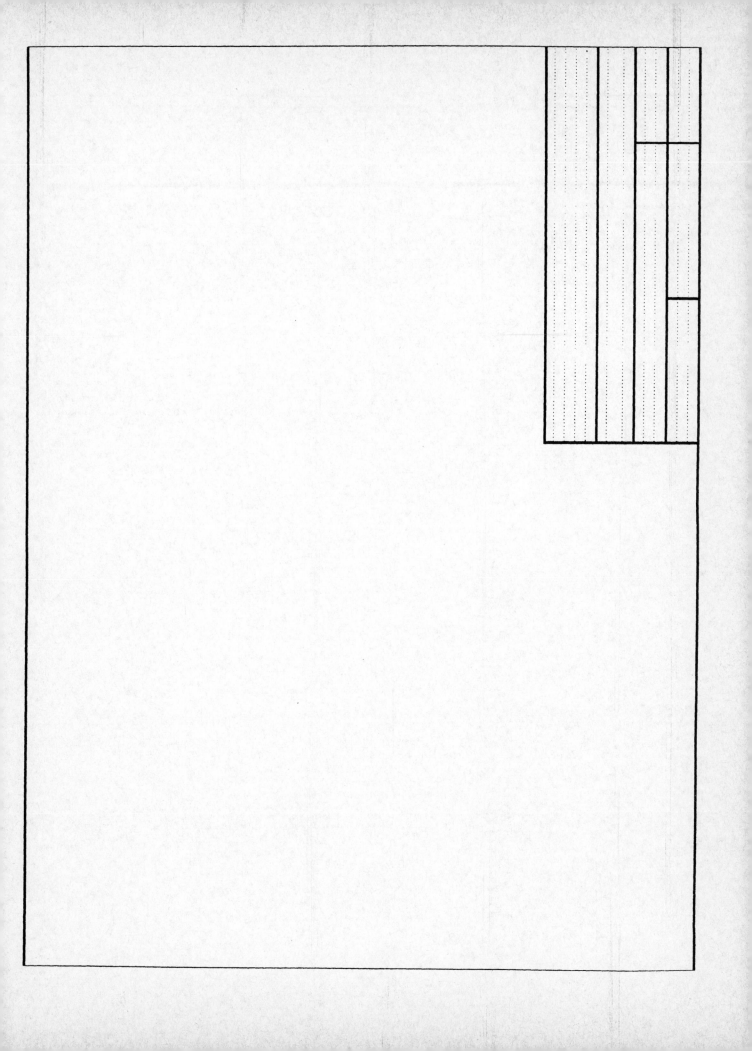

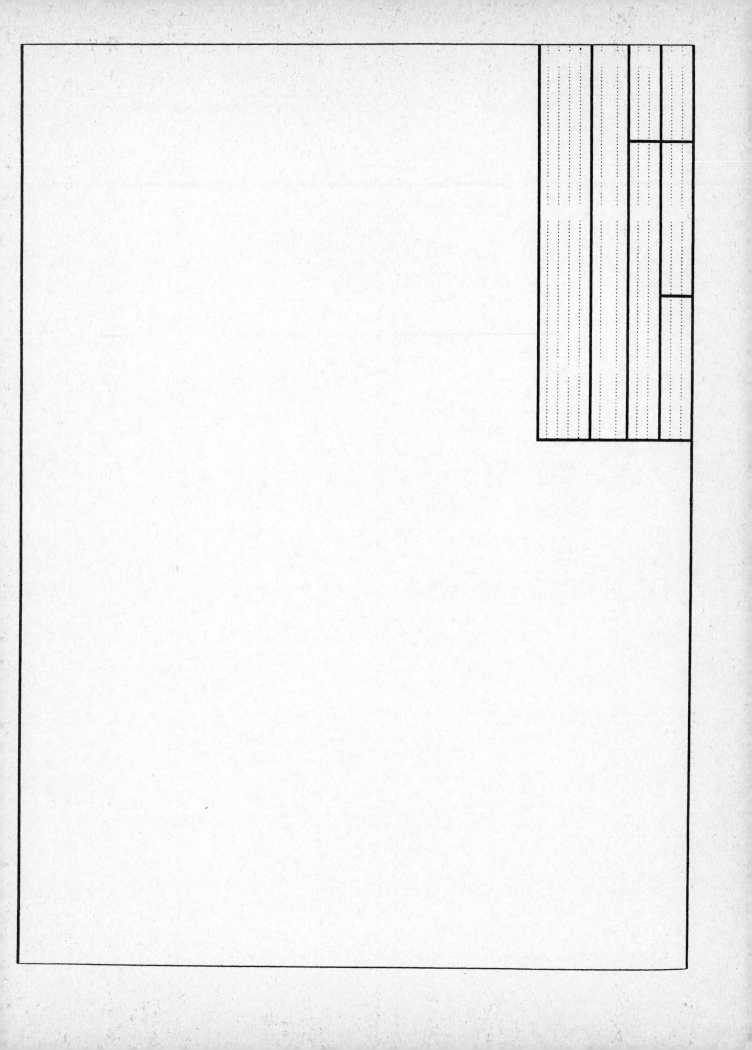

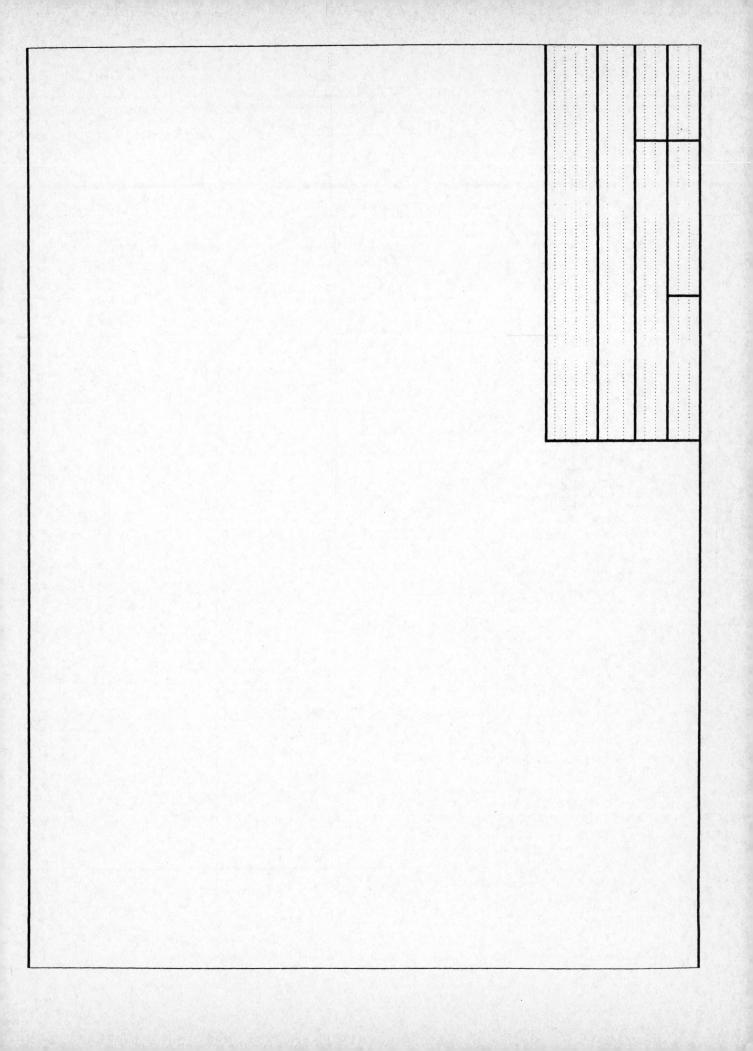